Department of Health and Welsh Office

# CODE OF PRACTICE

## Mental Health Act 1983

**Laid before Parliament in December 1989 pursuant to section 118(4) of the Mental Health Act 1983**

London: HMSO

# Contents

# PREFACE

This Code of Practice offers much detailed guidance on how the Mental Health Act 1983 should be implemented. Much of the Code will already be standard practice in many places. In others, changes to existing practices to conform to the Code can be made without any additional resources, simply by adopting new approaches to discharging responsibilities. Where adopting the recommendations of the Code would have significant resource implications, it is recognised that this can only be done as resources permit.

EL(90) P/85
LASSL(90) 5
WHC(90) 38
This circular is not part of the Code of Practice

# DEPARTMENT OF HEALTH

# WELSH OFFICE

Regional Health Authorities
District Health Authorities
Bethlem Royal and Maudsley Hospital
Special Hospitals Service Authority
Chief Executives of County Councils
        Metropolitan District Councils
        London Borough Councils
        The Common Council of the
          City of London
        The Council of the Isles of Scilly
Community Health Councils
Family Practitioner Committees

May 1990

**DEPARTMENT OF HEALTH AND WELSH OFFICE**

**CODE OF PRACTICE: SECTION 118 OF THE MENTAL HEALTH ACT 1983**

1.  The Code of Practice required under Section 118 of the Mental Health Act 1983 has now passed through the necessary Parliamentary procedure, and I attach copies for your information.

2.  All those using the Code of Practice should be aware of the statement made by Baroness Blatch on behalf of the Government

during the debate on the Code in the House of Lords on 29 January (Hansard Cols 68–86). The words 'where necessary' in paragraphs 2.27 and 2.30 are ambiguous. They should be interpreted as meaning that where a nearest relative is unaware of his or her rights under the Mental Health Act 1983, then either the approved social worker, or the doctor(s) involved in the patient's assessment should positively draw the nearest relative's attention to the existence and substance of these rights.

3. When the Code of Practice was debated in Parliament, the Government gave undertakings to seek the advice of the Mental Health Act Commission on the three specific criticisms raised during the debate, and on the operation of the new Code. The Department will then consult upon all the reactions and decide whether or not to lay alterations before Parliament. There may be further amendments from time to time, either to reflect developments in policy, or as a result of a request for amendments. The Department will similarly need to consult upon these and consider, in the light of the responses, whether or not to lay further amendments before Parliament. If Parliament agree to make amendments, the Code of Practice will be re-printed in full and will be available through H M S O.

4. The guidance contained in this Code is intended, primarily, to accommodate the needs, rights and entitlements of mentally disordered persons who are detained under relevant mental health legislation. However, much of the Code is equally applicable to informal patients, and practitioners should seek to ensure the Code is equally available to, and referred to as, a good practice document for the care and management of all mentally disordered patients.

5. Additional copies of the Code of Practice are available, as a priced document, through H M S O bookshops. There will be a discount for bulk orders.

6. Enquiries about the Code of Practice should be addressed to:

Robert Freeman
Department of Health
P H S 5
Alexander Fleming House
Elephant and Castle
London SE1 6BY

Jan Woodward
Welsh Office
H S S P 3B
Cathays Park
Cardiff CF1 3NQ

7. This Executive Letter/Local Authority Letter/Welsh Health Circular (though not the Code of Practice unless alterations to it are made – see paragraph 3 above) – will be reviewed on 30 June 1991.

S D CATLING
DEPARTMENT OF HEALTH (P H S 5)
ALEXANDER FLEMING HOUSE
ELEPHANT AND CASTLE
LONDON SE1 6BY

A G THORNTON
WELSH OFFICE (H S S P 3B)
CATHAYS PARK
CARDIFF CF1 3NQ

# 1 Introduction

1.1 This Code of Practice has been prepared in accordance with Section 118 of the Mental Health Act 1983 (the Act) by the Secretary of State for Health and the Secretary of State for Wales, after consulting such bodies as it appeared to them to be concerned, and laid before Parliament. This Act does not impose a legal duty to comply with the Code but failure to follow the Code could be referred to in evidence in legal proceedings.

1.2 The Code imposes no additional duties on statutory authorities. Rather it provides guidance to statutory authorities, Managers (who have defined responsibilities under the provisions of the Act) and professional staff working in health (including mental nursing homes) and social services on how they should proceed when undertaking duties under the Act.

1.3 The Code provides much detailed guidance, but this needs to be read in the light of the following broad principles, that people being assessed for possible admission under the Act or to whom the Act applies should:

- receive respect for and consideration of their individual qualities and diverse backgrounds – social, cultural, ethnic and religions;

- have their needs taken fully into account though it is recognised that, within available resources, it may not always be practicable to meet them;

- be delivered any necessary treatment or care in the least controlled and segregated facilities practicable;

- be treated or cared for in such a way that promotes to the greatest practicable degree, their self determination and personal responsibility consistent with their needs and wishes;

– be discharged from any order under the Act to which they are subject immediately it is no longer necessary.

1.4 This means, in particular, that individuals should be as fully involved as practicable, consistent with their needs and wishes, in the formulation and delivery of their care and treatment, and that, where linguistic and sensory difficulties impede such involvement reasonable steps should be taken to attempt to overcome them. It means that patients should have their legal rights drawn to their attention, consistent with their capacity to understand them. Finally, it means that, when treatment or care is provided in conditions of security, patients should be subject only to the level of security appropriate to their individual needs and only for so long as it is required.

1.5 The Code has been made as comprehensive as possible, but inevitably gaps will emerge and amendments and additions to the Code will need to be made as appropriate in the light of experience. The Secretaries of State are required to keep the Code under review.

1.6 Finally a note on presentation. An attempt has been made to draft the Code in such a way as to make it acceptable not only to those for whom the Act requires it to be written but also many patients, their families, friends and supporters. Throughout the Code, the Mental Health Act 1983 is referred to as the Act. Where there is reference to sections of other Acts, the relevant Act is clearly indicated. The glossary (page 111) either defines some of the words in the Code or refers to relevant sections of the Act where definitions can be found. Following the style of the Act, the Code uses the pronouns 'he' and 'his' to encompass both male and female.

# 2  Assessment

*(Paras 21–26 of Memorandum – see Glossary for details)*

**General**

2.1 This chapter is about the assessment by Approved Social Workers (A S Ws) and doctors of the needs of a person with mental health problems, where it may lead to an application for admission to hospital under the Mental Health Act 1983 (the Act).

2.2 Doctors and A S Ws must recognize that both have specific roles to play in assessment and should arrive at their own independent decisions. Such recognition should be underpinned by good working relationships based on knowledge and understanding of each others' professional roles and responsibilities; assessment should be carried out jointly unless good reasons prevent it (although it may be advantageous for each professional to interview the patient alone). An agreement should be reached between the professionals involved in the assessment process as to how their responsibilities can best be discharged.

2.3 The decision *not* to apply for admission under the Act should be clearly thought through, and supported, where necessary, by an alternative framework of care and/or treatment.

2.4 Everyone involved in assessment should be aware of the need to provide mutual support, especially where there is a risk of the patient causing serious physical harm (including, where necessary, the need to call for police assistance and how to use that assistance to minimise the risk of violence).

## Assessment for possible admission under the Mental Health Act

### 2.5 The objectives of assessment under the Mental Health Act

All those assessing for possible admission under the Act should ensure that:

a.  they take all relevant factors into account;
b.  they consider and where possible implement appropriate alternatives to compulsory admission;
c.  they comply with the legal requirements to the Act.

### The factors to be taken into account at assessment

2.6 In judging whether compulsory admission is appropriate, those concerned should consider not only the health and safety of the patient but also:

– the patient's wishes and view of his own needs;

– his social and family circumstances;

– his cultural background;

– the nature of the illness/behaviour disorder;

– what may be known about the patient by his nearest relative, any other relatives or friends and professionals involved, assessing in particular how reliable this information is;

– other forms of care or treatment including, where relevant, consideration of whether the patient would be willing to accept medical treatment in hospital informally or as an out-patient;

– the needs of the patient's family or others with whom the patient lives;

– the need for others to be protected from the patient;

– the impact that compulsory admission would have on the patient's life after discharge from detention;

– the burden on those close to the patient of a decision not to admit under the Act;

– the appropriateness of guardianship. (See chapter 13).

Ordinarily only then should the applicant (in consultation with the other professionals) judge whether the criteria stipulated in any of the admission sections are satisfied, and take the decision accordingly. In certain circumstances the urgency of the situation may curtail detailed consideration of all these factors.

**Informal Admission**

2.7 Where admission to hospital is considered necessary and the patient is willing to be admitted informally this should in general be arranged. Compulsory admission should, however, be considered where the patient's current mental state, together with reliable evidence of past experience, indicates a strong likelihood that he will change his mind about informal admission prior to his actual admission to hospital with a resulting risk to his health and/or safety or to other persons.

**Protection of Others**

2.8 In considering 'the protection of other persons' (see Sections 2(1)(b) and 3(2)(c)) it is essential to assess both the nature and likelihood of risk and what level of risk others are entitled to be protected from, taking into account:

– reliable evidence of risk to others;

– any relevant details of the patient's medical history and past behaviour;

– the degree of risk and its nature. Too high a risk of physical harm, or serious persistent phychological harm to others, are indicators of the need for compulsory admission;

– the willingness and ability to cope with the risk, by those with whom the patient lives.

**The Deteriorating Patient**

2.9 The assessment of a patient may legitimately involve consideration of any prognosis of future deterioration of his mental health based on the known history of the individual's mental disorder. Those assessing the patient must consider:

- the reliability of such evidence;

- the views of the patient and any relatives or friends living with the patient about his possible future deterioration;

- the impact that any future deterioration would have on relatives/friends (especially those living with the patient) including an assessment of his ability and willingness to cope;

- whether there are other methods of coping with such deterioration.

## Individual professional responsibility – the Approved Social Worker

2.10 It is important to emphasise that where an A S W is assessing a person for possible admission under the Act he has overall responsibility for co-ordinating the process of assessment and, where he decides to make an application, for implementing that decision. The A S W must, at the start of his assessment of the patient, identify himself to the patient, members of the family or friends present with the patient, and the other professionals involved in the assessment; explain in clear terms his role and the purpose of his visit, and ensure that the other professionals have explained their roles. A S Ws should carry with them at all times documents identifying them as A S Ws.

2.11 The A S W must interview the patient in a 'suitable manner'.
a.   where the patient and A S W cannot understand each other's language sufficiently, wherever practicable recourse should be had to a professional interpreter who understands the terminology and conduct of a psychiatric interview (and if possible the patient's cultural background);
b.   where another A S W with an understanding of the patient's language is available, consideration should be given to requesting him to carry out the assessment or assist the A S W assigned to the assessment;
c.   where the patient has difficulty either in hearing or speaking, wherever practicable an A S W with appropriate communi-

cation skills should carry out the assessment or assist the
A S W initially assigned to the case. Alternatively the A S W
should seek the assistance of a professional interpreter. Social
service departments should issue guidance to their A S Ws as
to where such assistance can be obtained;

d. the A S W should bear in mind the potential disadvantages of
a patient's relative being asked to interpret, and made a judgement as to whether this is appropriate in the circumstances;

e. where the patient is still unwilling or unable to speak to the
A S W (despite assistance from interpreters) the assessment
will have to be based on whatever information the A S W can
obtain from all reliable sources;

f. it is not desirable for a patient to be interviewed through a
closed door or window except where there is serious risk to
other people. Where there is no immediate risk of physical
danger to the patient or to others, powers in the Act to secure
access (Section 135) should be used;

g. where the patient is subject to the effects of sedative medication, or the short-term effects of drugs or alcohol, the A S W
should consult with the doctor/s and, unless it is not possible
because of the patient's disturbed behaviour and the urgency
of the case, either wait until, or arrange to return when, the
effects have abated before interviewing the patient. If it is not
realistic to wait, the assessment will have to be based on whatever information he can obtain from all reliable sources.

2.12 The patient should ordinarily be given the opportunity of
speaking to the A S W alone but if the A S W has reason to fear
physical harm he should insist that another professional sees the
patient with him. If the patient would like another person (for
example a friend) to be with him during the assessment and any
subsequent action that may be taken, then ordinarily the A S W
should assist in securing that person's attendance unless the
urgency of the case or some other proper reason makes it inappropriate to do so.

2.13 The A S W must attempt to identify the patient's nearest
relative (see Section 26 of the Act and paras 67–68 of the
Memorandum), and ensure that his statutory obligations (Section
11) to the nearest relative are fulfilled. In addition, the A S W
should where possible:

a. ascertain the nearest relative's views about the patient's needs and his (the relative's) own needs in relation to the patient;
b. inform the nearest relative of the reasons for considering an application for admission under the Mental Health Act and the effects of making such an application.

2.14 If the nearest relative objects to an application being made, for admission for treatment or guardianship, it cannot proceed at that time. The A S W may then need to consider applying to the county court for the nearest relative's 'displacement' (Section 29), and local authorities must provide proper assistance, especially legal assistance, in such cases. It is desirable for clear practical guidance on the procedures to be available, and this should be discussed with the relevant county courts.

2.15 Where the A S W is the applicant for the admission of a patient to hospital, he must discuss, in so far as the urgency of the case allows, with other relevant relatives and friends their views of the patient's needs, and should take them into account.

2.16 The A S W should consult wherever possible with other professionals who have been involved with the patient's care, for example home care staff or community psychiatric nurses (CPNs).

2.17 When the A S W has decided whether or not he will make an application for admission he should tell (with reasons):

– the patient;

– the patient's nearest relative (whenever possible);

– the doctor/s involved in the assessment.

When an application for admission is to be made the A S W should start planning how the patient is to be conveyed to hospital, (see chapter 11).

## Individual professional responsibility – the Doctor

2.18 The doctor should:
a. decide whether the patient is suffering from mental disorder within the meaning of the Act (Section 1) and assess its

seriousness and the need for further assessment and/or medical treatment in hospital;

b.  consider the factors set out above at 2.6, discussing his views with the applicant and the other doctor involved;

c.  specifically address the legal criteria for admission under the Mental Health Act and if he is satisfied provide a recommendation setting out those aspects of the patient's symptoms and behaviour which satisfy the legal criteria for admission.

d.  ensure that, where there is to be an application for admission, a hospital bed will be available.

## Medical Examination

2.19 A proper medical examination requires:

– direct personal examination of the patient's mental state taking into account its social, cultural and (where relevant) ethnic context;

– consideration of all available relevant medical information including that in the possession of others, professional or non-professional.

Where the patient and doctor cannot understand each other's language the doctor should, wherever practicable, have recourse to a professional interpreter, who understands the terminology and conduct of a psychiatric interview (and if possible the patient's cultural background).

2.20 If direct access to the patient is not immediately possible, and it is not desirable to postpone the examination in order to negotiate access, the relevant powers in the Act must be invoked, (Section 135) or consideration given to calling the police in order to see if they would exercise any relevant lawful power of entry.

2.21 It may not always be practicable for the patient to be examined by both doctors at the same time; but they should always discuss the patient with each other.

2.22 It is desirable for both doctors to discuss the patient with the applicant. It is essential for at least one of them to do so.

## Joint Medical Recommendations

2.23 Joint medical recommendation forms (forms 3 and 10) should only be used where the patient has been jointly examined by two doctors. It is desirable that they are completed and signed by both doctors at the same time.

2.24 In all other circumstances separate recommendation forms should be used (forms 4 and 11).

## The Second Medical Recommendation

2.25 Other than in exceptional circumstances, the second medical recommendation should be provided by a doctor with previous acquaintances of the patient. This should be the case even when the 'approved' doctor (who is, for example, a hospital based consultant) already knows the patient. Where this is not possible (for example the patient is not registered with a G P) it is desirable for the second medical recommendation to be provided by an 'approved' doctor.

## A decision not to apply for Admission

2.26 Most compulsory admissions require prompt action to be taken but it should be remembered that the A S W has up to 14 days from the date of first seeing the patient to make an application for admission for assessment or treatment. Where a decision not to apply for a patient's compulsory admission is taken the professionals concerned must decide how to implement those actions (if any) which their assessment indicate are necessary to meet the needs of the patient including, for example, the referral to other social workers or services within the social services department. It is particularly important that any C P N concerned with the patient's care be fully involved in the taking of such decisions. The professionals must ensure that they, the patient and (with the patient's consent) the patient's nearest relative and any other closely connected relatives have a clear understanding of any alternative arrangements. It is good practice for such arrangements to be recorded in writing and copies made available to all those who need them (subject to the patient's right to confidentiality).

2.27 The A S W must discuss with the patient's nearest relative the reasons for not making an application. Where necessary the A S W must advise the nearest relative of his rights to apply and suggest that he consult with the doctors if he wishes to consider this alternative. Where, moreover, the A S W is carrying out an assessment at the request of the nearest relative (Section 13(4)) the reasons for not applying for the patient's admission must be given to the nearest relative in writing. Such a letter should contain sufficient details to enable the nearest relative to understand the decision whilst at the same time preserving the patient's right to confidentiality.

## Particular Practice Issues

*Disagreements*

2.28 Sometimes there will be differences of opinion between assessing professionals. There is nothing wrong with disagreements: handled properly these offer an opportunity to safeguard the interests of the patient by widening the discussion on the best way of meeting the patient's needs. Doctors and A S Ws should be ready to consult colleagues (especially C P Ns and other community care staff involved with the patient's care), while retaining for themselves the final responsibility. Where disagreements do occur, professionals should ensure that they have set out to each other in discussion their views of the salient features of the case and their conclusions.

2.29 Where there is an unresolved dispute about an application for admission, it is essential that the professionals do not abandon the patient and the family. Rather, they should explore and agree an alternative plan, if necessary on a temporary basis, and ensure that the family is kept informed. It is desirable for such a plan to be recorded in writing and copies made available to all those who need it (subject to the patient's right to confidentiality).

*The choice of Applicant*

2.30 The A S W is usually the right applicant, bearing in mind professional training, knowledge of the legislation and of local

resources, together with the potential adverse effect that a nearest
relative application might have on the relationship with the
patient. The doctor should therefore advise the nearest relative
that it is preferable for an A S W to make an assessment of the
need for a patient to be admitted under the Act, and for the A S W
to make the application where necessary. The doctor should, however, if necessary advise the nearest relative of his Section 13(4)
(see 2.33) rights and of his right to make an application.

2.31 The doctor should never advise the nearest relative to make
the application in order to avoid involving an A S W in an
assessment.

## Agency Responsibilities

*The Local Authority*

2.32 A nearest relative should not be forced himself to make an
application for admission under the Act because it is not possible
for an A S W to attend for assessment. Subject to resources, local
authorities should aim to provide a 24 hour A S W service to
ensure that this does not happen.

2.33 *Section 13(4)*. Local authorities should:
a.   issue A S Ws with guidance on what amounts to a 'request'
     from a nearest relative;
b.   have explicit policies on how to respond to repeated requests
     for assessment where the condition of the patient has not
     changed significantly;
c.   give guidance to A S Ws, as to whether nearest relative
     requests can be accepted by way of general practitioners (G Ps)
     or other professionals. (Such requests should certainly be
     accepted provided the G P or other professional has been so
     authorised by the nearest relative.)

## Emergencies out of hours etc

2.34 Teams must pass on information to professional colleagues
who are next on duty to enable them to make necessary arrangements; for example where an application for admission is not

immediately necessary but might be in the future. For example, the necessary arrangements could then be made for an A S W to attend the next day.

## Interpreters

2.35 Local and health authorities should ensure that A S Ws and doctors respectively receive sufficient guidance on the use of interpreters, and should seek to make arrangements for there to be an easily accessible pool of professional interpreters. Authorities should consider cooperating in making this provision. (See 2.11(a) for further details.)

## The Health Authority

*Doctors approved under Section 12*

2.36 The Secretary of State for Health has delegated to regional health authorities, and the Secretary of State for Wales to district health authorities, the task of approving medical practitioners under Section 12(2).

2.37 Thus regional health authorities (in England) and district health authorities (in Wales) should:
a.  take active steps to encourage sufficient doctors, including G Ps to apply for approval;
b.  seek to ensure a 24 hour on-call rota of approved doctors sufficient to cover the area;
c.  maintain a regularly updated list of approved doctors which indicates how each approved doctor can be contacted and the hours that he is available;
d.  ensure that the up-to-date lists of approved doctors and details of the 24 hour on-call rota are circulated to all concerned parties including G Ps, mental health centres and social services.

2.38 Authorities should consider making part of the job description for new consultant psychiatrists with a responsibility for providing a catchment area service obligations to become approved under Section 12 of the Act, to keep such approval up-to-date and to participate in the 24 hour on-call approved doctors' rota.

## Health Authorities/Local Authorities

2.39 Health authorities and local social services authorities should cooperate in ensuring that regular meetings take place between professionals involved in mental health assessment in order to promote understanding, and to provide a forum for clarification of their respective roles and responsibilities.

# 3 Part III of the Mental Health Act – patients concerned with criminal proceedings

*Assessment*

## General

*Responsibility to Patients*

3.1 Those subject to criminal proceedings have the same right to psychiatric assessment and treatment as other citizens. The aim should be to ensure that everyone in prison or police custody in need of medical treatment for mental disorder which can only satisfactorily be given in a hospital as defined by the Act is admitted to such a hospital.

3.2 All professionals involved in the operation of Part III of the Act should remember:
a.   the vulnerability of people, especially those who are mentally disordered, when in police or prison custody. The risk of suicide or other self destructive behaviour should be of special concern;
b.   that a prison hospital is not a hospital within the meaning of the Act. Treatment facilities are limited, and the provisions of Part IV of the Act do not apply.

## Individual Professional Responsibilities

3.3 All professionals concerned with the operation of Part III of the Act should be familiar with:

– the relevant provisions of the Act and paragraphs of the Memorandum (paras 115 to 188);

– any relevant guidance issued by or under the auspices of the Home Office;

    – the responsibilities of their own and other disciplines and
authorities and agencies;

    – available facilities and services.

## Agency Responsibility

3.4 Regional health authorities/the Welsh Office should:
a. be able to provide to any requesting court (Section 39 Mental
Health Act), and also in response to any other proper request,
up-to-date and full information on the range of facilities for a
potential patient in hospitals, including secure facilities.
Facilities to which the patient might be admitted outside their
district or region may need to be specified and the arrangements for their funding clarified;
b. appoint a named person to respond to these requests.

3.5 Local authorities should appoint a named person to respond to
requests from the courts for them to consider the making of guardianship orders.

## Assessment by a doctor

3.6 Where a doctor is asked to provide an opinion in relation to a
possible admission under Part III of the Act:
a. he should identify himself to the person being assessed, and
explain at whose request he is preparing his report, discussing
any implications this may have for confidentiality;
b. he should have access to relevant social enquiry reports, the
inmate's medical record (where the defendant is remanded in
prison custody) and previous psychiatric treatment records as
well as relevant documentation regarding the alleged offence.
If he is not given any of this information he should say so
clearly in his report.

Where a doctor had previously treated the person it may be desirable for him to prepare the report. It would also be desirable for
the doctor (or one of them if two doctors are preparing reports) to
have appropriate beds at his disposal or where necessary to take
responsibility for referring the case to another doctor with access
to such facilities.

3.7 The doctor should where possible make contact with independant informants about the person's previous history, previous psychiatric treatment and patterns of behaviour.

3.8 Any assessment of the person is a medical responsibility. Appropriate members of the clinical team who would be involved with the individual's care and treatment may also be involved. It is often desirable for a nurse (who will be able to undertake a nursing assessment of the person's needs for nursing care and treatment and advise on whether he can be managed in the hospital) to accompany the assessing doctor where admission to hospital is likely to be recommended. The doctor should make contact with the social worker or probation officer who is preparing a social enquiry report, especially when psychiatric treatment is suggested as a condition of a probation order.

3.9 The doctor should not in his report anticipate the outcome of proceedings to establish guilt or innocence. It is sometimes appropriate to advise that a further report should be submitted to court after conviction and before sentencing. In any report prepared prior to conviction, the doctor may give advice on the appropriate disposal of the person in the event that he is convicted.

3.10 When the doctor has concluded that the person needs treatment in hospital, but there is no facility available, the task is not completed until:
a.  details of the type of provision required have been forwarded in writing to the district health authority, who will need detailed advice in order to discharge their responsibilities;
b.  in suitable cases contact has been made with the local N H S forensic psychiatrist.


**Role of A S W**

3.11 If an A S W has to be called to the prison or to a court to see a prisoner about to be released, with a view to making an application for admission as a detained patient under Sections 2 or 3, as much advance warning as possible should be given, and the A S W must be given ample time and facilities for interviewing the prisoner. The A S W should be given access to the social inquiry report as it is difficult within the confines of a prison/court to assess how a prisoner (convicted or on remand) might be able to benefit from alternative treatment in the community.

## Transfer of Prisoners to Hospital

3.12 The need for in-patient treatment for a prisoner must be identified and acted on swiftly, and contact made urgently between the prison doctor and the hospital doctor. The Home Office must be advised on the urgency of the need for transfer.

3.13 The transfer of a prisoner to hospital under the Act should not be delayed until close to his release date. A transfer in such circumstances may well be seen by the prisoner as being primarily intended to extend his detention and result in an unco-operative attitude towards treatment.

# 4 Private Practice and the Provision of Medical Recommendations

4.1 The Act restricts the provision of medical recommendations by certain categories of doctor in private practice. Thus:

a.  where an individual is to be admitted to a mental nursing home or as a private patient to a hospital, neither medical recommendation can be provided by a doctor on the staff of the hospital or mental nursing home (Section 12(3));

b.  no medical recommendation can be provided by a doctor who receives, or has an interest in the receipt of, any payment made on account of the maintenance of the patient (Section 12(5)(d)).

4.2 It is the personal responsibility of any doctor providing a medical recommendation to ensure that he is complying with these legal requirements; if in doubt legal advice must be sought.

4.3 It is undesirable for a doctor to provide a recommendation where he will receive payment from the patient (or a relative or friend or an insurance company) for his medical services after admission to hospital or a mental nursing home as a private patient.

4.4 If there could be any suspicion (however unjustified) that a doctor providing a medical recommendation is doing so for pecuniary advantage, then arrangements should be made for another doctor to do so.

4.5 Where the patient is currently receiving treatment from a doctor that doctor should be consulted by the doctor/s providing the medical recommendation.

# 5  Section 2 or Section 3

**The Choice**

5.1 Which admission Section should be used? Professional judgement must be applied to the criteria in each Section and **only** when this has been done can a decision be reached as to which, if either, Section applies.

5.2 **Section 2 pointers:**
a.  where the diagnosis and prognosis of a patient's condition is unclear;
b.  there is a need to carry out an in-patient assessment in order to formulate a treatment plan;
c.  where a judgement is needed as to whether the patient will accept treatment on a voluntary basis following admission;
d.  where a judgement has to be made as to whether a particular treatment proposal, which can only be administered to the patient under Part IV of the Act, is likely to be effective;
e.  where a patient who has already been assessed, and who has been previously admitted compulsorily under the Act, is judged to have changed since the previous admission and needs further assessment;
f.  where the patient has not previously been admitted to hospital either compulsorily or informally.

5.3 **Section 3 pointers:**
a.  where a patient has been admitted in the past, is considered to need compulsory admission for the treatment of a mental disorder which is already known to his clinical team, and has been assessed in the recent past by that team;
b.  where a patient already admitted under Section 2 and who is assessed as needing further medical treatment for mental disorder under the Act at the conclusion of his detention under

Section 2 is unwilling to remain in hospital informally and to consent to the medical treatment;

c. where a patient is detained under Section 2 and assessment points to a need for treatment under the Act for a period beyond the 28 day detention under Section 2. In such circumstances an application for detention under Section 3 should be made at the earliest opportunity and should not be delayed until the end of Section 2 detention. Such action may well deprive the patient of an opportunity to apply to a Mental Health Review Tribunal under Section 2. (Where such action is taken, then Managers should consider reviewing the patient's detention quickly (see chapter 24).)

5.4 Decisions should **not** be influenced by:

a. wanting to avoid consulting the nearest relative;

b. the fact that a proposed treatment to be administered under the Act will last less than 28 days;

c. the fact that a patient detained under Section 2 will get quicker access to a Mental Health Review Tribunal than one detained under Section 3.

# 6 Admission for assessment in an emergency (Section 4 of the Mental Health Act – paras 28 and 29 of the Memorandum)

**General**

6.1 An applicant cannot seek admission for assessment under Section 4 unless:
a. the criteria for admission for assessment are met, and
b. the matter is of urgent necessity and there is not enough time to get a second medical recommendation.

6.2 Section 4 is for genuine emergency and should never be used for administrative convenience. Those involved in the process of admission are entitled to expect 'second doctors' to be available so that they do not have to consider using Section 4 in circumstances other than genuine emergencies.

**Admission**

6.3 An emergency arises where those involved cannot cope with the mental state or behaviour of the patient. To be satisfied that an emergency has arisen, there must be evidence of:

– the existence of a significant risk of mental or physical harm to the patient or to others, and/or

– the danger of serious harm to property, and/or

– the need for physical restraint of the patient.

6.4 It is wrong for patients to be admitted under Section 4 rather than Section 2 because it is more convenient for the second doctor to examine the patient in, rather than outside, hospital. Those assessing an individual's need must be able to secure the attendance within a reasonable time of a second doctor and in particular an approved doctor.

6.5 If a 'second doctor' is not available to support an application under Section 2, an application under Section 4 cannot be made unless it is of urgent necessity.

6.6 If the A S W has no option but to consider an application for admission under Section 4 and is not satisfied with the reasons for the non-availability of the second doctor he must:
a.   discuss the case with the doctor providing the recommendation and seek to resolve the problem;
b.   if this is not possible, and the A S W has to make an application for admission under Section 4, have access to an officer in his local authority social services sufficiently senior to take up the matter with the health authority. The A S W's local authority should make it clear that the A S W in these circumstances is under an obligation to report the matter in this way.

6.7 The Managers should monitor the use of Section 4 and seek to ensure that second doctors are available to visit a patient within a reasonable time after being so requested.

6.8 If a patient is admitted under Section 4 an appropriate second doctor should examine him as soon as possible after admission, to decide whether the patient should be detained under Section 2.

# 7 Part III of the Mental Health Act – patient concerned with criminal proceedings

## *Admission*

### From Prison or Remand Centre

7.1 Where the receiving hospital does not already possess them the following must be sent at the time of the transfer:

> – an up-to-date medical report (sent by the prison medical officer to the patient's responsible medical officer (r m o));

> – any relevant social reports prepared by the probation service (addressed to the ward to which the patient has been admitted and marked for the attention of the relevant social worker or in their absence the patient's r m o).

It is important that all information is made available to the patient's r m o and other professional staff working with him.

### Restricted Patients

7.2 The Managers and the patient's r m o should ensure that where patients are admitted to hospital from prison under Sections 47 or 48 they have received and, as far as possible, understood the letter from the Home Office explaining their role in relation to restricted patients.

### Patients on Remand/Subject to an Interim Hospital Order

7.3 For patients detained under Sections 35, 36, 37 and 38 it is the court's responsibility to organise transport from the court to the receiving hospital. (See also 27.6.)

# 8  Doctors' holding power (Section 5(2))

*(Paras 30–32 of Memorandum)*

8.1 Good practice depends upon:

a.  the professionals involved in its implementation (and in particular the doctor invoking the holding power) correctly understanding the power and its purpose;

b.  the health authority/local social services authority making the necessary arrangements to ensure that when it is invoked the patient is fully assessed by an A S W and doctors for a possible admission under the Act;

c.  the Managers monitoring the use of the power.

**Nature of the Power**

8.2 The power (which authorises the detention of the patient **for up to** 72 hours) can only be used where the doctor in charge (or his nominated deputy) of an in-patient's treatment (including in-patients being treated for physical disorders) concludes that an application for admission under the relevant Sections of the Act is appropriate. The period of detention commences at the moment the doctor's report (form 12) is delivered to the Managers, or someone authorised to receive such a report on their behalf.

8.3 Any patient detained under Section 5(2) should be discharged from the order immediately:

a.  an assessment is carried out and a decision is taken not to make an application;

b.  the doctor decides that no assessment for possible admission needs to be carried out.

The power cannot be renewed, but circumstances can arise where, subsequent to its use and the patient's reversion to informal status, its use can be considered again.

8.4 An informal in-patient, for the purpose of this Section, is one who has understood and accepted the offer of a bed, who has freely appeared on the ward and who has co-operated in the admission procedure. The Section, for example, cannot be used for an out-patient attending a hospital's accident and emergency department.

8.5 Where a report under Section 5(2) is provided in relation to a patient under the care of a consultant other than a psychiatrist, the doctor invoking the power should make immediate contact with a psychiatrist.

8.6 Where a patient is receiving *treatment both for a physical disorder and a mental disorder*, in relation to Section 5(2) the doctor in charge of treatment is the consultant psychiatrist concerned.

## Information

8.7 Where a patient is detained under Section 5(2), the Managers must ensure that the requirements of Section 132 (information) are fulfilled.

## Treatment

8.8 Part IV of the Act does not apply to a patient detained under Section 5(2). In the absence of the patient's consent, therefore, treatment can only be given under the common law.

## The Doctor's Role

8.9 Section 5(2) should only be invoked if the use of Sections 2, 3 and 4 is not practicable or safe, i e Section 5(2) is not an admission Section under the Act.

8.10 The patient's doctor (or nominated deputy) must only use the power immediately after having personally examined the patient. No doctor should complete a Section 5(2) form and leave it on the ward with instruction for others to submit it to the Managers if, in their view, the patient is about to leave.

8.11 The patient may only be detained when the doctor's Section 5(2) report has been delivered to the Managers, or somebody authorized to receive it on their behalf (the doctor or nominated deputy must always be aware of who that person is).

## Assessment for admission while a patient is 'held' under Section 5(2)

8.12 All the normal rules apply, including the use of either Section 2 or Section 3 if compulsory admission is thought necessary.

## Nominated Deputies Section 5(3)

8.13 The registered medical practitioner in charge of an inpatient's treatment may nominate *one* deputy to exercise Section 5(2) powers in his place during his absence from the hospital. That deputy will then act on his own responsibility and should be reasonably experienced.

8.14 **Some safeguards**
a.   Where the nominated deputy is a junior doctor, the nominating doctor must be satisfied that his deputy has received sufficient guidance and training to carry out the function satisfactorily.
b.   Wherever possible the nominated deputy must contact the nominating doctor or another consultant (where the nominated deputy is not a consultant) before using Section 5(2). The nominated deputy should have easy access to the nominating doctor or the psychiatric consultant on-call.
c.   Only registered medical practitioners who are consultant psychiatrists should nominate deputies.
d.   The nominated deputy should report the use of Section 5(2) to his nominator as soon as possible.
e.   All relevant staff should know who is the nominated deputy for a particular patient.

8.15 *Remember* – it is unlawful for one nominated deputy to nominate another.

8.16 It is usual practice outside normal working hours for the nominated deputy to be the junior doctor on-call for the admission wards, the junior doctors being on duty on a rota basis. Where this occurs the nominating doctor is responsible for ensuring that he is prepared to nominate all the doctors liable to be on duty and that they are adequately trained, and that he has nominated an individual doctor for every duty period. Where the duty rota is changed during a period of duty and a new doctor comes on-call a change of nominated deputy must be agreed by the consultant in charge of the case or by the consultant on-call.

# 9 The nurse's holding power (Section 5(4))

*(Paras 33–34 of Memorandum)*

## The Power

9.1 A psychiatric emergency is no different from any other medical emergency; it requires the urgent attendance of a doctor. In practice, a doctor may not be immediately available. This chapter sets out the circumstances in which a registered mental nurse or a registered nurse for the mentally handicapped (first level) may lawfully prevent an informal in-patient receiving medical treatment for mental disorder from leaving the hospital – for up to 6 hours or until a doctor arrives, whichever is the earlier. It is the personal decision of the nurse and he cannot be instructed to exercise this power by anyone else. Part IV of the Mental Health Act does not apply to patients detained under Section 5(4).

## Assessment before Implementation

9.2 Before using the power the nurse should assess:
a. the likely arrival time of the doctor as against the likely intention of the patient to leave. Most patients who express a wish to leave hospital can be persuaded to wait until a doctor arrives, to discuss it further. Where this is not possible the nurse must try to predict the impact of any delay upon the patient;
b. the consequences of a patient leaving hospital immediately – the harm that might occur to the patient or others – taking into account:
   – what the patient says he will do;
   – the likelihood of the patient committing suicide;
   – the patient's current behaviour and in particular any changes in usual behaviour;
   – the likelihood of the patient behaving in a violent manner;

29

   – any recently received messages from relatives or friends;
   – any recent disturbance on the ward (which may or may
   not involve the patient);
   – any relevant involvement of other patients.
c. the patient's known unpredictability and any other relevant
   information from other members of the multi-disciplinary
   team.

## Acute Emergencies

9.3 Normally assessment should precede action but in extreme circumstances it may be necessary to invoke the power without carrying out the proper assessment. The suddenness of the patient's determination to leave and the urgency with which the patient attempts to do so should alert the nurse to potentially serious consequences if the patient is successful in leaving.

## Reports

9.4 The nurse (who must be entitled to use the power) invokes it by completing form 13. This must be delivered to the Managers (or an officer appointed by them) as soon as possible after completion. It is essential that:
a. the reasons for invoking the power are entered in the patient's nursing and medical notes;
b. a local incident report form is sent to the Managers.

9.5 At the time the power elapses the nurse must complete form 16.

## Use of restraint

9.6 A nurse invoking Section 5(4) is entitled to use the minimum force necessary to prevent the patient from leaving hospital. The general principles that should be applied when the use of restraint has to be considered are set out in paragraphs 18.7 and 18.8.

9.7 The nurse in charge of the ward should explain in private to the patient the need for using Section 5(4) and, when it occurs, the need to lock the ward door.

## Management Responsibilities

9.8 The use of Section 5(4) is an emergency measure and the doctor should treat it as such, arriving as soon as possible. If the doctor has not arrived within 5 hours the nurse should contact the consultant or the Unit General Manager (U G M), and one of the Managers should be informed. Either the U G M or the Manager should supervise the patient's leaving after the 6 hours if no doctor has attended. The doctor must not wait 6 hours before attending simply because that is the maximum time allowed.

9.9 The holding power lapses upon the arrival of the doctor.

9.10 A suitably qualified nurse should be on all wards where there is a possibility of Section 5(4) being invoked. Although the Section is more likely to have to be used on acute admission wards, and wards where there are acutely disturbed patients, or patients requiring intensive nursing care, local management must also assess the potential for its use elsewhere in the hospital or unit. As a result of such assessment they should ensure that suitable arrangements are in place for a suitably qualified nurse to be available should the power need to be invoked.

# 10 The police power to remove to a place of safety (Section 136)

***(Para 293 of Memorandum)***

**Good Practice**

10.1 This depends on:
a. the local social services authority, district health authority and the Chief Officer of Police establishing a clear policy for its implementation;
b. all professionals involved in its implementation understanding the power and its purpose and following the local policy concerning its implementation.

**The Local Policy**

10.2 The aim of the policy should be to secure the competent and speedy assessment by a doctor *and* an A S W of the person detained under the power.

10.3 The policy should define, in particular, the responsibilities of:
a. police officers to remain in attendance, where the patient's health or safety or the protection of others so require when the patient is taken to a place of safety (other than a police station);
b. police officers, doctors and A S Ws for the satisfactory returning to the community of the person assessed under Section 136 but not admitted to hospital or immediately placed in accommodation.

10.4 The policy should include provisions for the use of the Section to be monitored so that:
a. a check can be made of how it is being used, including its use in relation to particular categories of people or in particular circumstances;

b.   informed consideration can be given by all parties to the policy to any changes in the mental health services that might result in the reduction of its use.

## The Place of Safety

10.5 The identification of preferred places of safety is a matter for local agreement. Regard should be had to any impact different types of place of safety may have on the person held and hence on the outcome of an assessment.

## Good Practice Points

10.6 Where an individual is detained by the police under Section 136 it is desirable that:
a.   where he is to be taken to a hospital as a place of safety *immediate* contact is made by the police with both the hospital and the local social services department;
b.   where the police station is to be used as a place of safety immediate contact is made with the local social services authority and the appropriate doctor.

The local policy for the implementation of Section 136 should ensure that police officers have no difficulty in identifying whom to contact.

## Record Keeping

10.7 A record of the person's time of arrival must be made immediately he reaches the place of safety. As soon as the individual is no longer detained under Section 136 he must be so advised by those who are detaining him. It would be good practice for Managers (where the hospital is used as the place of safety) to devise and use a form for recording the end of the person's detention under this Section (similar to the form used for Section 5(4)).

10.8 Section 136 is not an emergency admission Section. It enables an individual who falls within its criteria to be detained for the purposes of an assessment by a doctor and A S W, and for any necessary arrangements for his treatment and care to be made. When these have been completed, within the 72 hour detention period, the authority to detain the patient ceases. Where a hospital is used as a place of safety it may be better for the patient not to be formally admitted although he may have to be cared for on a ward. Where such a policy is adopted it is essential to remember that the patient must be examined by a doctor in the same way as if he had been formally admitted.

## Information about Rights

10.9 Where an individual has been arrested by the police under Section 136:

a. the arrested person is entitled to have another person of his choice informed of his arrest and whereabouts. (Section 56 of Police and Criminal Evidence Act);

b. when the arrested person is in police detention (i e a police station is being used as a place of safety) he has a right of access to legal advice. (Section 58 of Police and Criminal Evidence Act);

c. where detention is in a place of safety other than a police station access to legal advice should be facilitated whenever it is requested.

10.10 Where the hospital is used as a place of safety the managers must ensure that the provisions of Section 132 (information) are complied with.

10.11 Where the police station is a place of safety, although Section 132 does not apply, it would be good practice for the policy referred to above to require that the same information is given in writing on the person's arrival at the place of safety.

## Assessment

10.12 Local implementation policy should ensure that the doctor examining the patient should wherever possible be 'approved'.

10.13 Assessment by both doctor and social worker should begin as soon as possible after the arrival of the individual at the place of safety. Any implementation policy should set target times for the commencement of the assessment and the health authority/local authority should review what happens in practice against these targets.

10.14 The person must be seen by *both* the doctor and the A S W. The local policy should include the necessary arrangements to enable the person wherever possible to be jointly assessed. If the doctor sees the person first and concludes that admission to hospital is unnecessary, or the person agrees to informal admission, the individual must still be seen by an A S W, who must consult with the doctor about any other necessary arrangements for his treatment and care that might need to be made. It is desirable for a consultant psychiatrist in mental handicap and an A S W with experience of working with mentally handicapped people to be available to make a joint assessment should there be a possibility that the detained person has a mental handicap.

10.15 The role of the A S W includes:

– interviewing the person;

– contacting any relevant relatives/friends;

– ascertaining whether there is a psychiatric history;

– considering any possible alternatives to admission to hospital;

– considering the need to make any other 'necessary' arrangements.

**Treatment**

10.16 Part IV of the Act does not apply to persons detained under Section 136. The person can only be treated in the absence of consent in accordance with provisions of the common law.

**Necessary Arrangements**

10.17 Once the assessment has been concluded it is the responsibility of the doctors and A S W to consider if any necessary arrangements for the person's treatment and care have to be made.

10.18 Where compulsory admission is indicated:

a.   where the hospital is the place of safety the person should be admitted either under Section 2 or Section 3 (whichever is appropriate). Wherever possible where the approved doctor providing one recommendation is on the staff of the hospital (as is usually the case) the second recommendation should be provided by a doctor with previous knowledge of the person (for example their G P). It has to be recognised that many people detained under Section 136 are not registered with a G P and in these circumstances as well as where it is not possible to secure the attendance of a G P who knows the person, it would be preferable for the second opinion to be provided by a second approved doctor;

b.   persons detained under Section 136 and who are formally admitted should not find their detention being continued under Section 5(2) or Section 5(4);

c.   where the police station is the place of safety then compulsory admission should be under Sections 2 or 3 (whichever is appropriate); but there may be exceptional circumstances where there is urgent necessity to remove the person to hospital, in which case Section 4 must be considered.

10.19 Section 136 provides the lawful authority for the removal by the police of a person to whom the provision applies, from a place to which the public have access. Where it is necessary to consider gaining access (and possibly removing to a place of safety) to a mentally disordered individual other than in a public place and where access is denied then consideration must be given to invoking the powers of entry under Section 135(1) or (2). Local authorities should issue guidance to A S Ws on how to invoke the power.

# 11 Conveying to hospital

*(Para 36 of Memorandum)*

**General**

11.1 Where an A S W is the applicant he has a professional responsibility for ensuring that all the necessary arrangements are made for the patient to be conveyed to hospital.

11.2 Where the nearest relative is the applicant, the assistance of an A S W is recommended and should be made available if requested. If this is not possible, other professionals involved in the admission should be prepared to give advice and assistance.

11.3 Authorities (including the ambulance service and the police) likely to be involved in conveying patients to hospital should prepare and publish joint policy/procedures to include:
a.  a clear statement of the roles and obligations of each authority and its personnel;
b.  the form of any authorization to be given by the A S W to others to convey the patient to hospital;
c.  guidance to personnel as to their powers in relation to conveying patients to hospital.

The local authority should take the lead in producing such guidance.

**The Approved Social Worker**

11.4 Where the approved social worker is the applicant he has a professional obligation to consider and then implement the most humane and least threatening method of conveying the patient consistent with ensuring that no harm comes to the patient or to others. He should ensure that the needs of the patient are not over-looked while trying to ensure that the legalities are observed. He should take into account:

- the patient's wishes;

- the views of concerned relatives or friends involved with his admission;

- the views of other professionals involved in the application or who know the patient;

- his judgement of the patient's state of mind, and the likeli-hood of the patient behaving in a violent or dangerous manner.

- the impact that any particular mode of conveying the patient will have on the patient's relationship with the community to which he will return.

11.5 The A S W is permitted to delegate the task of conveying the patient to another person (e g ambulance personnel or possibly the police). But the A S W retains ultimate responsibility to ensure that the patient is conveyed in a lawful and humane manner, and must be ready to give the necessary guidance to those asked to assist.

11.6 It will often be best to convey the patient by ambulance; the A S W will need to decide if he should accompany the patient. Where requested by the applicant, the ambulance authority should be willing to make the necessary arrangements. If the patient would prefer to be accompanied by another professional (perhaps better known to him) or by a responsible relative, the A S W may ask that person to escort the patient, provided he is satisfied that in doing so he is not increasing the risk of harm to the patient or others.

11.7 The patient should not be conveyed to hospital by car unless the A S W is satisfied the patient will not be a danger to himself or others. There should *always* be an escort for the patient other than the driver.

11.8 If the patient is likely to be violent or dangerous the police should be asked to help. Such a patient should never be conveyed by car. Where possible an ambulance should be used. Otherwise a police vehicle suitable for conveying such a patient should be used. While the police may have to exercise their duty to protect persons or property while the patient is being conveyed they should, where this is not inconsistent with their duty, comply with any directions or guidance given by the A S W.

11.9 The A S W should telephone the receiving hospital to ensure that the patient is expected and give the likely time of arrival. If possible he should ask the name of the person who will be formally receiving the admission documents.

11.10 The A S W must ensure that the admission documents arrive at the receiving hospital at the same time as the patient. If the A S W is not travelling in the same vehicle as the patient, the documents should be given to the person authorized to convey the patient with instructions for them to be presented to the officer authorized to receive them.

11.11 If the A S W is not travelling with the patient, he should arrive at the hospital at the same time or as soon as possible afterwards. He should ensure that the admission documents have been delivered, that the admission of the patient is under way and that any relevant information in his possession is passed to appropriate personnel in the hospital. He should remain in the hospital with the patient until he is satisfied that the patient has been detained in a proper manner.

11.12 A patient who has been sedated before being conveyed to hospital must be accompanied by a nurse or a doctor.

# 12   Receipt and scrutiny of documents

*(Paras 50–55 of Memorandum)*

12.1 The Managers should formally delegate their duties to receive and scrutinize admission documents to a limited number of officers with an adequate knowledge of the relevant parts of the Act. There must be adequate 24 hour cover. It is best that a general manager should take overall responsibility on behalf of the Managers for the proper receipt and scrutiny of documents.

12.2 There is a difference between 'receiving' documents and 'scrutinizing' them. Although it is desirable that documents should be scrutinized at the same time as they are received, circumstances will often dictate that in order for it to be done properly scrutiny should take place later.

**Receipt of Documents**

12.3 Some guiding rules:
a.   where the Managers' obligation to receive documents is delegated to nursing staff, such delegation should be to the nurse in charge of the ward. If the nurse is below the grade of first level nurse, he should seek the advice of a first level nurse when 'receiving' documents;
b.   the hospital should have a check list for the guidance of those delegated to receive documents, to ensure that they do not contain any errors which cannot be corrected at a later stage in the procedure (see Section 15);
c.   when the patient is being admitted on the application of an A S W the person 'receiving' the admission documents should check their accuracy with the A S W;
d.   the 'receiving' officer should have access to a manager for advice, especially at night.

## 'Scrutinizing' Documents

12.4 Some guidance rules:

a.  where the person delegated to receive the documents is not authorized by the Managers to rectify a defective admission document the documents must be scrutinised by a person so authorized immediately on the patient's admission (or during the next working day if the patient is admitted at night, weekends or public holidays when such a person is not available);

b.  the Managers must arrange for the medical recommendations to be medically scrutinized, to ensure that they show sufficient legal grounds for detention. The clinical description of the patient's mental condition should include a description of his symptoms and of his behaviour, not merely a diagnostic classification. This scrutiny should be carried out at the same time as the administrative scrutiny (see immediately above).

## Managers

12.5 Some guiding rules:

a.  the Managers are responsible for ensuring that patients are detained lawfully; they should therefore monitor the receipt and scrutiny of admission documents on a regular basis;

b.  those delegated to scrutinise documents must be clear about what kinds of errors on application forms and medical recommendations can and cannot be corrected (see paras 52–55 of Memorandum). If no original pink forms are available photocopies of an orginal form can be used;

c.  details of defective admission documents, whether rectifiable or not, and of any subsequent action, must be given to the Managers on a regular basis;

d.  Managers should ensure that those delegated to receive and scrutinize admission documents understand the requirements of the Act, and if necessary receive appropriate training.

# 13  Guardianship (Section 7)

*(Paras 43–48 of Memorandum)*

## Purpose of Guardianship

13.1 The purpose of guardianship is to enable patients to receive community care where it cannot be provided without the use of compulsory powers. It enables the establishment of an authoritive framework for working with a patient with a minimum of constraint to achieve as independent a life as possible within the community. Where it is used it must be part of the patient's overall care and treatment plan.

## Assessment for Guardianship

13.2 A S Ws and registered medical practitioners should consider guardianship as a positive alternative when making decisions about a patient's treatment and welfare. In particular it should be actively considered as an alternative both to admission to hospital and to continuing hospital care.

13.3 Any application for guardianship should be based on discussions among most professionals who are or who could be involved in the patient's care, and the A S W assessing the needs and appropriateness of guardianship. This should be by way of a multi-disciplinary case discussion, but if guardianship is to be considered as an alternative to admission it may not be possible to arrange such a meeting in the time available. It is important that any procedures instituted by social services departments are no more than the minimum necessary to ensure the proper use of guardianship and that guardianship can be used in a positive and flexible manner. Any application for guardianship should be accompanied by a comprehensive care plan established on the basis of multi-disciplinary discussions.

## Components of effective Guardianship

13.4 A comprehensive care plan is required which identifies the services needed by the patient, including as necessary his care arrangements, appropriate accommodation, his treatment and personal support requirements and those who have responsibilities under the care plan. The care plan should indicate which of the powers given by the guardianship order are necessary to achieve the plan. If no power is considered necessary for achieving any part of the care plan guardianship is inappropriate.

13.5 There will need to be the following components:
a. A recognition by the patient of the 'authority' of the guardian. There must be a willingness on the part of both parties to work together within the terms of the authority which is vested in the guardian by the Act;
b. the guardian should be willing to 'advocate' on behalf of the patient in relation to those agencies whose services are needed to carry out the care plan;
c. readily available support from the local authority for the guardian;
d. an appropriate place of residence taking into account the patient's needs for support, care, treatment and protection;
e. access to necessary day care, education and training facilities;
f. effective cooperation and communication between all persons concerned in implementing the care plan;
g. commitment on the part of all concerned that care should take place in the community.

## Duty of Social Services Department

13.6 Each local authority should prepare and publish policy setting out the arrangements for:
a. receiving, considering and scrutinising applications for guardianship. Such arrangements should ensure that applications are adequately, but *speedily*, considered;
b. monitoring the progress of the guardianship including steps to be taken to fulfil the authority's statutory obligations in relation to private guardians and to arrange visits to the patient;

c.   ensuring the suitability of any proposed private guardian and that the private guardian understand and carry out their statutory duties, including the appointment of a nominated medical attendant;

d.   ensuring that patients under guardianship receive, both orally and in writing, relevant aspects of the same information that health authorities are required to give to detained patients under Section 132;

e.   ensuring, in particular, that the patient is aware of his right to apply to a Mental Health Review Tribunal and that a named officer of the local authority will give any necessary assistance to the patient in making such an application;

f.   maintaining detailed records relating to the person under guardianship;

g.   ensuring the review of the patient's detention under guardianship towards the end of each period of detention;

h.   discharging the guardianship order rather than allowing it to lapse.

**The powers of the Guardian**

13.7 Section 8 of the Act sets out the three powers of the guardian as follows:

a.   to require the patient to live at a place specified by the guardian. This does not provide the legal authority to detain a patient physically in such a place, nor does it authorize the removal of a patient against his wish. If the patient is absent without leave from the specified place he may be returned within 28 days by those authorized to do so under the Act;

b.   to require the patient to attend at specified places for medical treatment, occupation, education or training. If the patient refuses to attend the guardian is not authorized to use force to secure such attendance, nor does the Act enable medical treatment to be administered in the absence of the patient's consent;

c.   to require access to the patient to be given at the place where is living to persons detailed in the Act. A refusal without reasonable cause to permit an authorized person to have access to the patient is an offence under Section 129. Neither the guardian nor any authorized person can use force to secure entry.

If the patient consistently resists the exercise of the guardian's powers it can be concluded that guardianship is not the most appropriate form of care for that person and the guardianship order should be discharged.

### 13.8 (Points to remember:)

a. guardianship does not restrict the patient's access to hospital services on a voluntary basis. If the patient should require treatment and there is no need to detain for treatment, he may be admitted informally and may remain under guardianship unless discharged or transferred;

b. the guardianship order can also remain in force if the patient is admitted to hospital under Sections 2 or 4. It does not remain in force if the patient is admitted for treatment under Section 3.

c. it is possible in certain circumstances for a patient liable to be detained in hospital by virtue of an application under Part II of the Act to be transferred into guardianship and for a person subject to guardianship under Part II of the Act to be transferred into the guardianship of another local social services authority or person approved by such authority or to be transferred to hospital. (See Section 19 and rules 7–9 of the Mental Health (Hospital, Guardianship and Consent to Treatment) Regulations 1983.)

### 13.9 Particular Practice Issues:

a. guardianship must not be used to require a patient to reside in hospital save in very exceptional circumstances where it is necessary for a very short time in order to provide shelter whilst a place of residence in the community is being obtained.

b. where an adult is assessed as requiring residential care but due to mental incapacity is unable to make a decision as to whether he wishes to be placed in residential care, those who are responsible for his care should consider the applicability and appropriateness of guardianship for providing a framework within which decisions about his current and future care can be planned. Guardianship should never be used solely for the purpose of transferring an unwilling person into residential care.

## Guardianship under Section 37

13.10 As a potentially useful alternative to hospital orders, courts are empowered to make guardianship orders where the prescribed criteria, which are similar to those of a hospital order, are met and the court having regard to all the circumstances considers reception into the guardianship of the local social services authority, or of any other person, appropriate. Guardianship orders may be particularly suitable in helping to meet the needs of mentally impaired offenders who could benefit from occupation, training and education in the community. Before making such an order the court has to be satisfied that the local authority or person is willing to act as guardian. The local authority will need to be satisfied with the arrangements and in considering the appropriateness of guardianship they will be guided by the same principles as apply under Part II of the Act. Similarly the powers and duties conferred on the local authority or private guardian and the provisions as to duration, renewal and discharge are those which apply to guardianship applications except that the power to discharge is not available to the nearest relative.

# 14  Information

**(Paras 274–278 of the Memorandum)**

## General

14.1 All patients should be given, throughout their stay in hospital, as much information as possible about their care and treatment. Additionally it should be made clear to informal patients that they are allowed to leave hospital at any time. Subject to the requirements of the Act, information should be given in a suitable manner and at a suitable time to ensure that the patient understands as much as possible. Requests for information from the patient should be encouraged and answered honestly and comprehensively. Periodic checks should be made to ensure that patients continue to understand the information given to them. The purpose of information is to help people understand why they are in hospital. In particular it is important that informal patients understand their right to leave hospital. The Department of Health publishes leaflets about the information required to be given under Section 132.

## Statutory Information

14.2 Section 132 requires the Managers to take all practical steps to ensure that *all* detained patients are given and understand:
a.  specific information as soon as is practicable after their admission (see Section 132 and para 274);
b.  particular information in so far as it is relevant to the patient (see Section 132(2) and para 275).

14.3 The Managers are also required to ensure that the above information is given in writing to the patient's nearest relative – unless the patient wishes otherwise. (The patient must be asked before any information is given to the nearest relative.)

14.4 Section 133 requires that (unless the patient objects) the nearest relative should, if practical, be given at least seven days notice of a detained patient's discharge from hospital or mental nursing home, especially if he is going to be involved in the aftercare of the patient.

## The Managers' Information Policy

14.5 In carrying out their statutory responsibilities the Managers will need to devise a system which ensures that:
a.  the right information is given to the patient;
b.  the information is given in a suitable manner and at a suitable time in accordance with the requirements of the law;
c.  the person who is to give the information is identified in relation to each detained patient. The Managers will need to ensure that staff know what information is to be given and that they have received sufficient training and guidance to enable them to give it;
d.  a record is kept of the information given;
e.  a check is made that information has been properly given to each detained patient.

14.6 The Managers should ensure that a member of staff is designated to check the patients records regularly to ensure that all information has been given at the appropriate times, and that it has been repeated as necessary. This officer should also be available to give advice to those whose job it is to give information.

14.7 As far as practicable, the Managers (if appropriate in co-operation with the relevant local authorities) should ensure that an interpreter service is set up which, in addition to making use of interpreters in the community, would invite staff members with appropriate language skills to offer their assistance, and make appropriate training available to them.

## Who should give the Information

14.8 The Managers will need to delegate someone within the patient's multi-disciplinary team to give the information. This should be a flexible arrangement; for example, there will be cases where a patient may have a special rapport with a particular member of staff to whom the task could be delegated. But the Managers retain the ultimate responsibility for complying with the statutory requirements.

## Patients with hearing impairment

14.9 The information giver should seek the assistance of a local authority or voluntary agency social worker for the deaf. In case of difficulties the advice of the British Deaf Association or the Royal National Institute for the Deaf should be sought.

## Patients with visual impairment

14.10 The statutory information should be made available to them either in braille (where appropriate) or on tape. In the case of difficulties the Royal National Institute for the Blind should be asked for advice.

## Recording

14.11 The person giving the advice should record on the patients' case notes all details about the information given, the various attempts to give it, patients' reactions, and an assessment of their comprehension at every stage in the procedure. This will not only serve as a record of compliance with the requirements of Section 132 but also as an aide-memoire for staff.

## Particular Information

14.12 Certain events which will arise in the course of the patient's stay in hospital will need to be appropriately explained. Some of them are set out below:

a.  *Consent to treatment.* The patient must be informed, in terms which he is likely to understand, of the nature, purpose and likely effects of the treatment proposed. (See chapter 15). Patients must be advised of their rights to withdraw consent to treatment at any time before its completion and of the need for them to give fresh consent to treatment thereafter. If relevant a detained patient should be told how his refusal, or withdrawal of consent can be over-ridden by the second opinion process operated by the Mental Health Act Commission and, where treatment has begun, of the doctor's power to continue it on an urgent basis if the discontinuance would cause serious suffering to the patient. (These explanations should be the responsibility of medical and nursing staff.)

b. *Renewal of detention and transfer to informal status.* A patient may need to be told of the provision in the Act under which he is detained and of its effect; care should be taken to ensure that the patient does not assume that he will be discharged on expiry of the current detention period nor that his detention will automatically be renewed. All future possibilities and options should be explained as early as possible. When the Managers are considering the renewal of a patient's detention order, the patient should be told that he has a right to be heard by them, and advised how he may exercise this right. Administrative staff should be responsible for these explanations. The patient should also be advised of his right to ask the Managers to consider his discharge.

c. *Applications to Mental Health Review Tribunals.* There is a statutory obligation on the Managers to tell a detained patient of his right to apply to a mental health review tribunal. In addition, Managers should regard it as an obligation to ensure that patients and their nearest relatives know of the existence and role of these tribunals and of their respective rights of application to them. The Managers should ensure that patients remain aware of their rights to apply to a tribunal and are given every opportunity and assistance to exercise those rights, including facilities for representation. The patient should be told of his right to be represented by a lawyer of his choice, the Law Society's Mental Health Review Tribunal representation panel list and about other appropriate organisations, and should be given every assistance in using any of them. Managers should designate a member of staff to see personally every detained patient who applies to a tribunal or who is referred to a tribunal and to give them every reasonable assistance in securing representation (if the patient wishes).

d. *The Mental Health Act Commission.* There is a statutory obligation to advise patients about the Mental Health Act

Commission. In addition patients should be made aware of visits made by the Commissioners to hospitals and of the opportunities which they will then have to meet the Commissioners. The Managers should also ensure that detained patients know that they have a right to complain to the Commission about their detention, treatment or general care, if they are not satisfied with the investigation of a complaint made to the Managers. Notices of visits of the Mental Health Act Commission should be prominently displayed and individual patients notified wherever possible.

e. *Other information.* Information-givers must bear in mind the need to give other information which could assist the patient, for example, the name of his r m o, the name of the member of the general manager's staff to whom he can turn, how to complain and, as far as part III patients are concerned, the possibility of considering an appeal against the sentence.

# 15 Medical Treatment

**(Paras 189–205 of Memorandum)**

## Introduction

15.1 Everyone involved in the medical treatment of mental disorder should be familiar with the provision of Part IV of the Act, related statutory instruments, relevant circulars and advice notes. But it is for the r m o or the doctor in charge of treatment to ensure that the Act's provisions relating to medical treatment are complied with.

15.2 The Managers should arrange to monitor compliance with the provisions of Part IV of the Act. (For a more detailed discussion of Part IV of the Act see chapter 16.)

## Medical Treatment

15.3 For the purposes of the Act, medical treatment includes 'nursing and also includes care, habilitation and rehabilitation under medical supervision,' i e the broad range of activities aimed at alleviating, or preventing a deterioration of, the patient's mental disorder. It includes physical treatment such as E C T and the administration of drugs, and psychotherapy.

## Treatment Plans

15.4 These are essential for both informal and detained patients. Consultants should coordinate the formulation of the treatment plan in consultation with their professional colleagues. The plan should be recorded in the patient's clinical notes.

15.5 A plan of treatment should include a description of the immediate and long-term goals for the patient with a clear indication of the treatments proposed and the methods of treatment. The patient's progress and possible changes to the plan should be reviewed at regular intervals.

15.6 Wherever possible the whole plan should be discussed with the patient, with a view to him making his own contribution and saying whether or not he agrees with it. It is also important to discuss it with the appropriate relatives concerned about a patient (but only with his consent).

**Consent to Treatment**

15.7 The common law, as it relates to consent to treatment, applies to all patients informal or detained, except where statute (for example Part IV of the Act) specifically overides it.

15.8 Before an individual can be given medical treatment his valid consent is required except where the law (either the common law or statute law) provides the lawful authority to treat the patient without consent. The position is that treatment can be given without consent, when the patient is incapable of giving consent by reason of the fact that he is:

a.  an immature child, in which case, a parent or person having parental authority may consent;
b.  unconscious and is in urgent need of treatment to preserve life, health or well-being (unless there is unequivocal and reliable evidence that the patient did not want that treatment), provided that the treatment has to be administered while the patient is still unconscious;
c.  suffering from a mental disorder which is leading to behaviour that is an immediate serious danger to himself or to other people and it is not possible immediately to apply the provisions of the Mental Health Act (where treatment is a proper response in order to achieve the minimum necessary to avert that danger);
d.  otherwise incapable and in need of medical care in circumstances in which he has not declared his unwillingness to be treated prior to the onset of the incapacitating condition.

In all cases involving the treatment of an individual incapable of giving consent, the treatment must be 'in the patient's best interest,' i e:

 – necessary to save life or prevent a deterioration or ensure an improvement in the patient's physical or mental health;

 – in accordance with a practice accepted at the time by a responsible body of medical opinion skilled in the particular form of treatment in question.

There may be exceptional circumstances in which the proposed treatment should not be carried out on incapable patients without the approval of the High Court. Sterilisation, according to the House of Lords in Re F (1989) may be one such circumstance (see 15.17).

15.9 'Consent' is the voluntary and continuing permission of the patient to receive a particular treatment, based on an adequate knowledge of the purpose, nature, likely effects and risks of that treatment including the likelihood of its success and any alternatives to it. The assessment of the patient's ability to make a decision about his own treatment and the nature and extent of the information to be given in seeking consent are matters for clinical judgement, guided by current professional practice and subject to legal requirements. Permission given under any unfair pressure is not 'consent.'

15.10 The fact that a person is suffering from a mental disorder does not mean that he is thereby incapable of giving consent. Capacity to consent is variable in mental disorder and varies over time in any one person; not everyone is equally capable of understanding the same explanation of a treatment plan. A person is more likely to be able to give valid consent if the explanation is appropriate to the level of assessed ability. This does not necessarily mean that an individual should be given less information. Thus, the capacity to consent should be assessed in relation to the particular patient, at the particular time, as regards the particular treatment proposed.

15.11 The information which must be given should be related to the particular patient, the particular treatment and relevant medical knowledge and practice. In every case sufficient information must be given to ensure that the patient understands in broad terms the nature, likely effects and risks of that treatment including the likelihood of its success and any alternatives to it. Additional information is a matter of professional judgement for the doctor proposing the treatment. The patient should be invited to ask questions and the doctor should answer fully, frankly, and truthfully. There may be a compelling reason, in the patient's interests, for not disclosing certain information. A doctor who chooses not to disclose must be prepared to justify the decision. If a doctor chooses not to answer a patient's question, he should make this clear so that the patient knows where he stands.

15.12 The patient should be told that his consent to treatment can be withdrawn at any time and that fresh consent is required before further treatment can be given or reinstated. The patient should receive an explanation of the likely consequences of not receiving treatment. (See 16.14 on withdrawing consent in relation to treatment administered under Part IV of the Act.)

15.13 It is the duty of everyone proposing to give treatment to use reasonable care and skill, not only in giving information prior to seeking a patient's consent but also in meeting the continuing obligation to provide the patient with adequate information.

## Capacity to make a decision

15.14 The assessment of a patient's capacity to make a decision about his own medical treatment is a matter for clinical judgement, guided by current professional practice and subject to legal requirements. It is the personal responsibility of any doctor proposing to treat a patient to determine whether the patient has capacity to give a valid consent.

## The Basic Principles

15.15 An individual in order to have capacity must be able to:

  – understand what medical treatment is and that somebody has said that he needs it and why the treatment is being proposed;

- understand in broad terms the nature of the proposed treatment;

- understand its principal benefits and risks;

- understand what will be the consequences of not receiving the proposed treatment;

- possess the capacity to make a choice.

It must be remembered:

- any assessment as to an individual's capacity has to be made in relation to a particular treatment proposal;

- capacity in an individual with a mental disorder can be variable over time;

- all assessments of an individual's capacity should be fully recorded in the patient's medical notes.

## Incapacity and medical treatment

15.16 The administration of medical treatment to people incapable of taking their own treatment decisions is understandably a matter of continuing concern to professionals and others involved in the care of such people. It is the personal responsibility of professionals to ensure that they understand the relevant law.

15.17 The House of Lord's decision in *In Re F*([1989] 2 WLR 1025; [1989] 2 All ER) helped to clarify the common law in relation to general medical and surgical treatment of people who lack the capacity to give consent. It held that a doctor may lawfully operate on or give treatment to a person who lacks the capacity to give consent provided that it is in the best interests of the patient, i e being necessary to save life, or to prevent a deterioration, or ensure an improvement, in his physical or mental health. However, as a matter of practice, an operation for sterilisation should not be performed on an adult who lacks the capacity to give consent without first obtaining the opinion of the court that the operation is, in the circumstances, in the best interests of the person concerned. The means of doing this is by seking a declaration that the operation is lawful (see paragraph 15.18). The standard of care required of the doctor concerned in all cases is that laid down in *Bolam v Friern Hospital Management Committee* [1957] 1 WLR 582, namely, that he must act in accordance with a responsible and competent body of relevant professional opinion.

15.18 The procedures to be used when applying for a declaration that a proposed operation for sterilisation is lawful were set out by Lord Brandon of Oakbrook in *In Re F:*

i. applications for a declaration that a proposed operation on or medical treatment for a patient can lawfully be carried out despite the inability of such patient to consent thereto should be by way of originating summons issuing out of the Family Division of the High Court;

ii. the applicant should normally be those responsible for the care of the patient or those intending to carry out the proposed operation or other treatment, if it is declared to be lawful;

iii. the patient must always be a party and should normally be a respondent. In cases in which the patient is a respondent the patient's guardian ad litem should normally be the Official Solicitor. In any cases in which the Official Solicitor is not either the next friend or the guardian ad litem of the patient or an applicant he shall be respondent;

iv. with a view to protecting the patient's privacy, but subject always to the judge's discretion, the hearing will be in chambers, but the decision and the reasons for that decision will be given in court.

The Official Solicitor has also issued a Practice Note concerning applications to the High Court concerning sterilisation (New Law Journal October 13 1989, page 1380.)

15.19 The forthcoming revision of the *Handbook of Contraceptive Practice* will consider the effect of *In Re F* on operations for sterilisation, as well as other matters relating to the sexuality of people with a mental handicap.

15.20 The Law Commission plans to review aspects of the law relating to mental incapacity in its Fourth Programme of Law Reform (Cm 800.)

# 16 Medical Treatment and Second Opinions

*(Paras 189–205 of Memorandum)*

**General**

16.1 Part IV of the Act provides specific statutory authority for forms of medical treatment for mental disorder to be given to most patients liable to be detained without their consent in certain circumstances and with certain safeguards. It also provides specific safeguards. Patients liable to be detained are those who are detained or have been granted leave of absence (Section 17). It also provides specific safeguards to all patients when treatments are proposed that give rise to special concern.

16.2 Its provisions can be summarized as follows:

a. *Treatments requiring the patient's consent and a second opinion (Section 57)* – psychosurgery and the surgical implantation of hormones for the suppression of male sexual drive (exceptionally these safeguards apply to all patients)

b. *Treatments requiring the patient's consent or a second opinion (Section 58)* – the administration of medicine beyond three months, and treatment by E C T at any time. These safeguards apply to all patients liable to be detained except those detained under S 4, S 5(2) or (4), S 35, S 135, S 136 and S 37(4); also patients conditionally discharged under S 42(2) and S 73 and 74. All these patients can only be treated under common law

c. *Treatments that do not require the patient's consent (Section 63)* – all medical treatments for mental disorder given by or under the direction of the patient's responsible medical officer and which are not referred to in Section 57 or 58 (this provision applies to the same patients as S 58)

d. *Urgent treatment (Section 62)* – in certain circumstances the provisions of Section 57 and 58 do not apply where urgent treatment is required (see para 16.17 below).

16.3 Everyone involved in the operation of Part IV of the Mental Health Act should be familiar with:
a.  the provisions of Part IV of the Act;
b.  paragraphs 189–205 of the Memorandum;
c.  D H S S circular D D L(84)4;

In addition r m os should obtain copies of 'Advice to Second Opinion Appointed Doctors' published by the Mental Health Act Commission.

16.4 Detained status of itself does not imply inability to give consent. For all treatments proposed for a detained patient, and which may be lawfully given under the Act, it is necessary first to seek the patient's agreement and consent. It is the personal responsibility of the patient's r m o to ensure that the patient's valid consent has been sought and the interview at which such consent was sought should be properly recorded.

16.5 Part IV of the Act applies only to medical treatment for mental disorder. Treatments for physical disorder therefore cannot be given under this part of the Act unless it is a physical disorder that gives rise to a mental disorder and it is necessary to treat the physical disorder in order to treat the mental disorder.

## Treatments requiring Consent and a Second Opinion (Section 57)

16.6 Section 57 reflects public and professional concern about particular forms of treatment; such treatments need to be considered very carefully in view of the possible long-term effects and the ethical issues that arise. Procedures for implementing this Section must be agreed between the Mental Health Act Commission and the hospitals concerned.

16.7 Before the r m o or doctor in charge of treatment refers the case to the Mental Health Act Commission:
a.  the referring doctor should personally satisfy himself that the patient is capable of giving valid consent and has consented;
b.  the patient and (if the patient agrees) his family and others close to him should be told that the patient's willingness to undergo treatment does not necessarily mean that the decision

59

to proceed has yet been taken. The patient should be made fully aware of the provisions of Section 57;

c.  for psychosurgery the consultant considering the patient's case should have fully assessed the patient as suitable for psychosurgery;

d.  for psychosurgery, the patient's case should be referred to the Commission prior to his transfer to the neuro-surgical centre for the operation. The Commission will usually visit and interview the patient at the referring hospital at an early stage in the procedure;

e.  for surgical implantation of hormones for the purpose of reducing male sexual drive, the relationship of the sexual disorder to mental disorder, the nature of the treatment, the likely effects and benefit of treatment and knowledge about possible long-term effects require considerable care and caution should be taken.

16.8 It should be remembered that Section 57 only refers to the surgical implantation of hormones for the suppression of male sexual drive where it is administered as a medical treatment for mental disorder; and that, if there is any doubt as to whether it is a mental disorder which is being treated, independent legal and medical advice must be sought. The advice of the Mental Health Act Commission should also be obtained.

**Treatments requiring Consent or a Second Opinion (Section 58)**

16.9 When E C T is proposed valid consent should always be sought by the patient's r m o:

a.  if the patient consents the r m o should complete form 38 and include on the form the proposed maximum number of applications of E C T. Such information should be included in the patient's treatment plans: this can be done by the second opinion appointed doctor (S O A D);

b.  if the patient's valid consent is not forthcoming the r m o (in the event that he wishes to proceed with the treatment) must comply with the requirements of Section 58, which should be initiated as soon as possible.

## Medication before 3 months

16.10 This period starts on the occasion when medication for mental disorder was first administered by any means. The patient's r m o must ensure that the patient's valid consent is sought prior to the administration of any medication. If such consent is not forthcoming or is withdrawn during this period, the r m o must consider if he wishes to proceed in the absence of consent, consider alternative treatments or give no further treatment.

## Medication after 3 months (Section 58)

16.11 At the end for the three month period referred to above the patient's r m o should personally seek the patient's consent to continuing medication, and such consent should be sought for any subsequent administration of medication. If the patient consents, the r m o must certify accordingly (form 38). The r m o should indicate on the certificate the drugs proposed, by the classes described in the British National Formulary (indicating the dosages if they are above the B N F advisory maximum limits) and the method of their administration. If the patient's consent is not forthcoming the r m o must comply with the safeguard requirements of Section 58 (although for urgent treatment Section 62 may apply).

## The 3 months Rule

16.12 The 3 month period gives time for the doctor to create a treatment programme suitable for the patient's need. Although the patient can be treated in the absence of consent during this period no such treatment should be given in the absence of an attempt to obtain valid consent. The three month period is not affected by renewal of the detention order, withdrawal of consent, leave or change in or discontinuance of the treatment. A fresh period will only begin if there is a break in the patient's liability for detention.

16.13 If medication is likely to be continued beyond the 3 month period the need for consent or a second opinion should be foreseen in good time. The r m o should satisfy himself at all time that consent remains valid.

## Withdrawal of Consent

16.14 A patient subject to the provisions of Part IV of the Act may withdraw consent at any time. Fresh consent or the implementing of Section 58 procedures is then required before further treatment can be carried out or re-instated. Where the patient withdraws consent he should receive a clear explanation (recorded in the patient's records) of:

– the likely consequences of not receiving the treatment;

– (where applicable) that a second medical opinion under Part IV of the Act may or will be sought in order to authorize treatment in the continuing absence of the patient's consent;

– (where applicable) the doctor's power to begin or continue treatment under Section 62 until a second medical opinion has been obtained.

## Treatments not requiring the patient's Consent (Section 63)

16.15 Apart from treatments specifically mentioned in Sections 57 and 58, other forms of medical treatment for the mental disorder for which the patient is suffering (so long as they are given by or under the direction of the patient's r m o) may be given without the patient's consent being required (although it should always be sought). Section 63 covers a wide range of therapeutic activities involving a variety of professional staff and includes in particular psychological and social therapies (see Section 145 for a definition of medical treatment).

16.16 In practice, it is unlikely that most of these activities could be undertaken without the patient's acceptance and active cooperation. Acceptance in relation to such procedures requires a clear expression of agreement between the patient and the therapist before the treatment has begun, such agreement being expressed positively in terms of willingness to co-operate rather than as a consequence of passive submission.

## Urgent Treatment

16.17 Any decision to treat a patient urgently under Section 62 is a responsibility of the patient's r m o who should bear in mind the following considerations:

a.   treatment can only be given where it is immediately necessary to achieve one of the objects set out in Section 62 and it is not possible to comply with the safeguards of Part IV of the Act. It is insufficient for the proposed treatment to be simply 'necessary' or 'beneficial;'

b.   in certain circumstances 'hazardous' or 'irreversible' treatment cannot be administered under this section even if it is immediately necessary. The patient's r m o is responsible for deciding whether treatment falls into either of these categories, having regard to mainstream medical opinion.

c.   urgent treatment given under Section 62 can only continue for as long as it is immediately necessary to achieve the statutory objective(s);

d.   before deciding to give treatment under Section 62 the patient's r m o should wherever possible discuss the proposed urgent treatment with others involved with the patient's care;

16.18 The Managers should ensure that a form is devised to be completed by the patient's r m o every time urgent treatment is given under Section 62. Such a form should require details to be given of the proposed treatment; why it is of urgent necessity to give the treatment; the length of time for which the treatment was given. The Managers should monitor the use of Section 62 in their hospitals.

## Review of Treatment (Section 61)

16.19 *All* treatments (whether or not Section 61 applies to them) should be regularly reviewed and the patient's treatment plan should include details of when this will take place. When a patient has been treated under Section 57 and when a second doctor has authorized treatment in the absence of the patient's consent under Section 58 a review by the Mental Health Act Commission on behalf of the Secretary of State has to take place:

a.  in the circumstances set out in Section 61 (all professionals involved should be familiar with the procedures for completing form M H A C 1);

b.  where the S O A D has time limited his certificate or made his certificate conditional upon making of a review report on the treatment at a date earlier than the first statutory review (See M H A C 1).

16.20 When submitting a report under Section 61, the r m o should advise the Mental Health Act Commission if a patient for whom a certificate of second opinion has previously been issued has since given his consent and the consent is still valid. After a receipt of a review report, the Mental Health Act Commission will, when required, send an appointed doctor to reassess the patient and decide whether the treatment should continue.

## The Second Opinion Appointed Doctor (S O A D) and Part IV

16.21 Promoting the welfare of the patient by the implementation of Part IV and its safeguards requires careful planning and management. The patient's r m o is personally responsible for ensuring that Part IV procedures are followed in relation to that patient;

16.22 Overall responsibility for ensuring that the powers and duties of the Act are lawfully obeyed rests with the Managers who should ensure that proper arrangements are made to enable r m os to discharge their responsibilities, but all professional staff involved with the implementation of Part IV of the Act should be familiar with its provisions and the procedures for its implementation in the hospital.

16.23 Patients have a statutory right to be informed about the provisions of Part IV of the Act as it relates to them. They should be reminded by letter in addition to receiving the statutory leaflet when either their consent to treatment is needed or a second opinion is due.

### Arranging the visit of the S O A D

16.24 Where it is required, the patient's r m o has the personal responsibility of ensuring that the request for the visit of a S O A D is made. He should ensure that the arrangements are made with the Mental Health Act Commission.

### Preparing for the S O A D's visit

16.25 The patient's treatment proposal (together with any records of discussion among relevant professional staff) must be given to the S O A D before or at the time of his visit. The Managers in consultation with the r m o are responsible for ensuring that the patient is available to meet the S O A D and that the following people are available in person (although it is recognised that in exceptional circumstances this may not be possible) at the time the S O A D visits:

- the patient's r m o;
- the statutory 'consultees.' (See 16.32);
- any other relevant persons.

And that the following documents are available:

- the primary copies of the patient's detention documents;
- all the patient's case notes (records of past responses to similar treatment are very important).

It is desirable that a single professional record is kept for each patient which contains all records relating to that patient. Adequate facilities must be made available for the visit.

### The visit of the S O A D

16.26 During his visit the S O A D should:
a.  in the case of a treatment under Section 58, satisfy himself that the patient's detention papers are in order;
b.  interview the patient in private (but others may attend if the patient and the S O A D agree or if it is concluded that the doc-

tor would be at significant risk of physical harm from the patient);

c.   discuss the case with the patient's r m o face to face, though in exceptional circumstances where telephone consultation will suffice;

d.   consult with other persons professionally concerned with the patient's care as statutorily required (i e the 'statutory consultees'). The S O A D should be prepared, where appropriate, to consult a wider range of persons professionally concerned with the patient's care than those required by the Act and (with the patient's consent) the patient's nearest relative or other appropriate relatives or supporters.

16.27 The S O A D may not be able to reach a decision at the time of the first visit. In these circumstances the patient should be told of the delay.

16.28 Once a decision has been reached, it is the r m o's responsibility to inform the patient of the S O A D's decision.

16.29 If the r m o and the S O A D are unable to reach agreement, the patient's r m o should be informed by the S O A D personally at the earliest opportunity. It is good practice for the S O A D to give reasons for his dissent and every attempt should be made to reach agreement. Neither doctor should allow a disagreement in any way to prejudice the interests of the patient. If agreement cannot be reached, the position should be recorded in the patient's case notes by the r m o who will continue to have responsibility for the patient's management. The opinion given by S O A Ds is their personal responsibility. It cannot be appealed against to the Mental Health Act Commission.

16.30 If the patient's situation subsequently changes the r m o may contact the Mental Health Act Commission and request a further second opinion. In these circumstances it is the policy of the Commission to ask the same S O A D to return.

## Roles and Responsibilities – the Hospital Managers

16.31 In anticipation of, and preparation for, a consultation under Part IV, the Managers and their staff should ensure that:

a. the statutory documents are in order and available to the S O A D;

b. a system exists for reminding the r m o prior to the expiry of the limit set by Section 58 and Section 61 and for checking the doctor's response;

c. a system exists for reminding the patient towards the expiry of the '3 month period' that his consent or a second opinion is required;

d. appropriate personnel are available for consultation. The need for there to be a person other than a doctor or nurse professionally concerned with the patient's care must be foreseen and their involvement initiated well in advance of any consultation.

**Roles and responsibilities – the 'Statutory Consultees.'**

16.32 The S O A D must consult:

a. a nurse, who must be qualified (nursing assistants, auxillaries and aides are excluded) and who has been professionally concerned with the patient's care;

b. another person similarly concerned who is neither a nurse nor a doctor. A student nurse, nursing aide, auxilliary or assistant would not be permissable under this latter category but a social worker, occupational therapist, psychologist, psychotherapist etc would be.

16.33 Any person who the S O A D proposes to consult must decide if he is sufficiently concerned professionally with the patient to fulfil the function. If he feels that another person is better placed to fulfil the function, or he is not qualified, he should make this known to the patient's r m o and the S O A D in good time.

16.34 Both consultees may expect a private discussion (only in exceptional cases on the telephone) with the S O A D and to be listened to with consideration.

16.35 Amongst the issues that the 'consultees' should consider commenting upon are:

– the proposed treatment and the patient's ability to consent to it;

- other treatment options;

- the way in which the decision to treat was arrived at;

- the facts of the case, progress, attitude of relatives etc;

- the implications of imposing treatment upon a non-consenting subject and the reasons for the patient's refusal of treatment;

- any other matter relating to the patient's care on which the 'consultee' wishes to comment.

'Consultees' should ensure that they make a record of their consultation with the S O A D which is placed in the patient's records.

## The role of the S O A D

16.36 The role of the S O A D is to provide an additional safeguard to protect the patient's rights. He must at the time of the interview determine whether the patient is capable of consenting and giving valid consent, or if the patient does not give his consent or is not capable of giving his consent, whether the treatment proposed by the patient's r m o is likely to alleviate or prevent a deterioration in the patient's condition and should be given.

16.37 The S O A D acts as an individual and must reach his own judgement as to whether the proposed treatment is reasonable in the light of the general consensus of appropriate treatment for such a condition. In reaching his judgement he should consider not only the therapeutic efficacy of the proposed treatment but also (where a capable patient is withholding his consent) the reasons for such withholding, which should be given their due weight.

16.38 The S O A D should seek professional opinion about the nature of the patient's disorder and problems, the appropriateness of various forms of treatment, including the proposed treatment, the patient's likely response to different types of treatment especially if based on previous experience of comparable treatment of a similar episode of disorder. He should give due weight to the opinion, knowledge, experience and skill of those consulted. He will have to sign form 39 before treatment may be given without consent. He may direct that a review report on the treatment be sent from the Mental Health Act Commission at a date earlier than the next date for review under Section 61.

# 17 Part III of the Mental Health Act – Patients concerned with Criminal Proceedings

## *Treatment and Care in Hospital*

### Patients on Remand to hospital under Sections 35 and 36

17.1 A patient who is remanded to hospital for reports or for treatment is entitled to obtain, at his own expense, an independent report on his medical condition from a registered medical practitioner chosen by him for the purpose of applying to court for the termination of the remand. Managers should help in the exercise of this right.

17.2 The consent to treatment provisions of the Act do not apply to patients remanded under Section 35, so treatment can only be administered in the absence of the patient's consent in an emergency under the provisions of the common law. (See Chapter 15).

17.3 Where a patient remanded under Section 35 is thought to be in need of medical treatment for mental disorder under Part IV of the Act consideration should be given to referring the patient back to court as soon as possible with an appropriate recommendation, and with an assessment of whether the patient is in a fit state to attend court. If there is delay in securing a court date (for example an order under Section 36 can only be made by a Crown Court and there can be a considerable delay before the patient is committed to the Crown Court), and depending on the patient's mental condition, consideration should be given to whether the patient meets the criteria of Section 3 of the Act.

17.4 A report prepared in pursuit of a Section 35 remand order should contain:

   — a statement as to whether a patient is suffering from a specified form of mental disorder as required by the Section, identifying its relevance to the alleged offence. The report must not anticipate the outcome of proceedings to establish guilt or innocence, and it may be right to suggest that a further report be submitted to the court between (possible) conviction and sentence;

— relevant social factors;

— any recommendations on care and treatment, including where and when it should take place and who should be responsible.

**Information**

17.5  The Managers have a duty to give information to the patient's nearest relative (unless the patient objects). This should be exercised with care; while in prison the patient will have been invited to give details of parents or next of kin, but this may not be the 'nearest relative' under the Act.

# 18 Patients Presenting Particular Management Problems

18.1 Patients, (both detained and informal) or people who may become patients, may behave in such a way as to disturb others around them; or their behaviour may present a risk to others around them or those charged with their care. Such disturbed behaviour may occur anywhere, and the issues addressed here relate to general health care settings as well as psychiatric facilities.

## Behaviour contributing to problems in management

18.2 The majority of people do not behave in a disturbing way, and professionals should not assume that a previous history of disturbance means that the patient will always behave that way. Professionals should also recognise that though they may experience the disturbed behaviour as intermittent, fellow residents or carers will experience it through 24 hours. Tolerance to irritating or disturbed behaviour is clearly related to exposure to it, and professionals should not categorise behaviour as disturbed without taking account of the circumstances under which it occurs.

18.3 Behaviour which can give rise to managerial problems can include:

— refusal to participate in treatment programmes;

— prolonged verbal abuse and threatening behaviour;

— destructive behaviour;

— self-injurious behaviour;

— physical attacks on others.

**Possible causes**

18.4 In exploring preventive methods staff should be aware of some possible, often very evident causes of problem behaviours:

— boredom and lack of environmental stimulation;

— too much stimulation, noise and general disruption;

— overcrowding;

— antagonism, aggression or provocation on the part of others;

— a generally unsuitable mix of patients;

— the rewarding of undesirable behaviour by attention.

**General preventive measures**

18.5 In addition to individual care plans much can be done to prevent behaviour problems by examining the ward or other environment and pinpointing problem areas. Among such general measures are:

— keeping patients fully informed of what is happening and why;

— giving each patient a defined personal space and a secure locker for the safekeeping of possessions;

— ensuring access to open space;

— organising the ward (in hospital) to provide quiet rooms, recreation rooms and visitors' rooms;

— ensuring access to a telephone;

— providing structured activities by professional staff;

— encouraging energetic activities for younger patients;

— providing training for staff in the management of disturbed behaviour;

— monitoring the mix of patients;

— developing nurse-patient allocation systems;

— consistent application and monitoring of any individual programme;

— ensuring that patients' complaints are dealt with quickly and fairly.

## Restraint

18.6 Restraint may take many forms and may vary in degree from a mild instruction to seclusion. The essence of restraint is to contain or limit another person's freedom. The most common reasons for restraint are:

— physical assault;

— destructive behaviour;

— non-compliance with treatment;

— self harm or risk of physical injury by accident;

— extreme and prolonged over-activity likely to lead to physical exhaustion.

## Basic principles

18.7 The basic principles which should underlie any methods which are aimed at reducing and eliminating unwanted behaviour are:
a.  by intervention, to reduce such behaviour;
b.  to review regularily any intervention as part of the patient's agreed treatment programme relating to his particular management problem;

Where it is likely that, in a group of patients, problem behaviour may appear unpredictably, an agreed strategy for dealing with the unanticipated events should be developed.

## Training

18.8 Staff in N H S hospitals and private mental nursing homes who are ordinarily likely to find themselves in situations where control and restraint might be necessary should attend an appropriate course run by a qualified instructor.

## Methods of Restraining Behaviour

18.9 *Physical restraint* should be used as little as possible, only as a last resort and never as a matter of course. It should be used in an emergency when there seems to be a real possibility that significant harm would occur if intervention is withheld. Any initial attempt to restrain aggressive behaviour should, as far as the situation will allow, be non-physical:

a.   assistance should be sought by call system or verbally;
b.   one member of the team should assume control of the incident;
c.   the patient should be approached where possible and agreement sought to stop the behaviour, or to comply with a request;
d.   where possible an explanation should be given of the consequences of refusing the request from staff to desist;
e.   other patients or people not involved in the use of restraint should be asked to leave the area quietly.

18.10 Where non-physical methods have failed or the incident is of such significant to warrant immediate action, the person in control of the incident may decide to restrain the patient physically. In doing so the following rules should be borne in mind:

a.   make a visual check for weapons;
b.   nominate staff members to assist in control and allocate each a specific task;
c.   a large number of staff grabbing at people can be counter-productive;
d.   fewer, but well briefed staff are likely to be more effective;
e.   aim at restraining arms and legs from behind if possible, seek to immobilise swiftly and safely;
f.   constantly explain reason for action and enlist support from patient for voluntary control as soon as possible.
g.   avoid neck holds;
h.   avoid excess weight being placed on any area, but particularly stomach and neck;
i.   do not slap, kick or punch.

Any restraint must be 'reasonable in the circumstances'. It must be the minimum necessary to deal with the harm that needs to be prevented.

## Medication

18.11 The control of behaviour by medication requires careful consideration. The judicious use of appropriate medication to reduce excitement and activity in order to facilitate other interventions can be an important adjunct to an individual programme. But medication which begins as purely thereapeutic may, by prolonged routine administration, become a method of restraint. It is therefore necessary to review each individual case and consider at the outset whether, where medication would have to be administered by force, it would be lawful and thereapeutic in the longer term. Medication should not be used as an alternative to adequate staffing levels.

18.12 The Authority should appoint a senior manager, possibly the nominated complaints officer, who should be informed of any patient who is being subjected to any form of restraint that lasts for more than two hours. On receipt of such information, such an officer should as soon as practicable see the patient and then, at regular interviews, make contact with the patient to ascertain if he has any complaints and to assist in putting them forward. In certain circumstances it may be desirable for the officer to devolve this responsibility to another person professionally concerned with the patient's case and with whom the patient has a good working relationship.

## Policy on Restraint

18.13 Health authorities should have clear, written policies on the use of restraint.

## Seclusion

18.14 Seclusion is the supervised confinement of a patient alone in a room which may be locked for the protection of others from significant harm. It is not a procedure that is specifically regulated by statute. Seclusion should be used as little as possible and for the shortest possible time. Many hospitals have discontinued its use. Seclusion should not be used as a punitive measure or to enforce good behaviour. Although it falls within the definition of medical treatment in the Mental Health Act, (Section 145), seclusion is not a treatment technique and should not feature as part of any treatment programme. Its use therefore cannot be foreseen. It should not be used because of staff shortages or because, for example, equipment is being damaged. Seclusion is a last resort, when all reasonable steps have been taken to avoid its use. It should never be used where there is a risk that the patient may take his own life or otherwise harm himself; its sole aim therefore is to contain severely disturbed behaviour which is likely to cause harm to others.

18.15 Hospitals should have clear written guidelines on the use of seclusion, distinguishing between seclusion and time-out, see chapter 19. The guidelines should contain instructions on environmental standards, the roles and responsibilities of all members of staff, the procedures for recording, monitoring, reviewing and follow-up. The aim of the guidelines should be to ensure the safety and well-being of the patient in a dignified and humane environment. The Managers should refer to a D H S S document 'Review of Special Hospitals Seclusion Procedures' published in April 1985.

**Procedure for Seclusion**

18.16 The decision to use seclusion can be made in the first instance by a doctor, the nurse in charge of the ward, a nursing officer or senior nursing officer. Where the decision is taken by someone other than a doctor, then the necessary arrangements must be made for a doctor to attend immediately.

18.17 A nurse should be readily available within sight and sound of the seclusion room at all times throughout the period of the patient's seclusion, and present at all times with a patient who has been sedated.

18.18 The aim of observation is to ascertain the state of the patient and whether seclusion can be terminated. The level should be decided on an individual basis, but a documented report must be made every 15 minutes.

18.19 *If seclusion needs to continue* a review should take place every 2 hours, carried out by 2 nurses in the seclusion room, and every 4 hours by a doctor. If seclusion continues for more than 8 hours consecutively or for more than 12 hours intermittently over a period of 48 hours, an independent review must take place with the r m o, a team of nurses and other health care professionals who were not directly involved in the care for the patient at the time the incident which led to the seclusion took place. If there is no agreement on ensuing action the matter should be referred to the unit general manager.

## Conditions of Seclusion

18.20 Seclusion should be in a safe, secure and properly identified room, where the patient cannot harm himself, accidentally or intentionally. The room should have adequate heating, lighting, ventilation and seating. It is a matter for local judgement what the patient is allowed to take into the room, but he should always be clothed.

18.21 The room should offer complete observation from the out-side, while also affording the patient privacy from other patients.

## Record Keeping

18.22 Detailed records should be kept in the patient's case notes of any use of seclusion, the reasons for its use and subsequent activity, cross-referenced to a special seclusion book or forms which should contain a step-by-step account of the seclusion procedure in every instance. The principal entry should be made by the nurse in charge of the ward and the record should be countersigned by a doctor and a unit nursing manager. The Managers should monitor and regularly review the use of seclusion.

## Locking Ward Doors on Open Wards

18.23 The management, security and safety of patients should, wherever practicable, be ensured by means of adequate staffing. Authorities are responsible for trying to ensure that staffing is adequate to prevent the need for the practice of locking patients in wards, individual rooms or any other area.

18.24 The nurse in charge of any shift is responsible for the care and protection of patients and staff, and the maintenance of a safe environment. At his discretion, he may decide for all or part of the shift for which he is responsible to lock the door of the ward because of the behaviour of a patient or patients to keep the environment safe. When doing this he should:
a.  inform all staff of why he is taking this action and how long it will last;
b.  inform the patient or patients whose behaviour has led to the ward door being locked of the reason for taking such action;
c.  inform all other patients that they may leave on request at any time and ensure that someone is available to unlock the door;
d.  inform his line manager of his action;
e.  inform the r m o or nominated deputy;
f.  keep a record of this action and reasons, and make use of an incident reporting procedure.

18.25 When handing over to the relieving shift he should discuss in detail the reasons for his action. Where the relieving nurse considers it necessary to keep the door locked, (a) to (e) above apply. Where any ward is locked for three consecutive shifts (excluding night duty) the Unit General Manager should be informed.

## Locked Wards and Secure Areas

18.26 There are some detained patients in ordinary psychiatric hospitals for whom professional judgement, or a requirement of a Court as an alternative to imprisonment, may point to the need for varying degrees of security. In such cases, where the need for physical security is a prerequisite to treatment, the patient's r m o, in consultation with the multi-disciplinary team should ensure that:

a. he has carefully weighed the patient's individual circumstances and the degree of danger involved;
b. he has carefully assessed the relative clinical considerations of placing the patient in a physically secure environment; in addition to or as opposed to providing care by way of intensive staffing;
c. treatment in secure conditions lasts for the minimum necessary period;
d. the patient's bed on an open ward is retained at all times to minimise any delay to his returning there.

18.27 It would be desirable for authorities to ensure that:
a. a ward/area are specifically designated for this purpose with appropriate staffing levels;
b. written guidelines are provided, setting out and clearly distinguishing between the categories of patient where it is appropriate to use physically secure conditions and those where it is not. The guidelines should include a clear policy for the practice, proper procedures and safeguards, the justification for its use and the circumstances in which it can be used;

## Deprivation of day-time clothing

18.28 Patients should never be deprived of appropriate day-time clothing during the day, with the intention of restricting their freedom of movement. They should not be deprived of other aids necessary for their daily living.

## Staff

18.29 Staff must try and get to know patients not only in order for the patient to gain confidence in them but also so that they can learn to recognise potential danger signs in patients and be able to diffuse the situation in time. They should have good communication skills and know when to intervene in certain potentially aggressive situations. Continuity of staffing is an important factor both in the development of professional skills and consistency in managing patients.

**Managers**

18.30 Staff involved in control and restraint may experience a degree of stress. Managers should ensure that they are given the opportunity to discuss these issues with them (the Managers) and with colleagues. Managers should formulate and make available to health and local authority staff, and local authority management a clear written operational policy on all forms of restraint.

# 19  Psychological Treatments

## Psychological Treatments

19.1 Psychological treatment techniques are widely used in the treatment of people suffering from mental disorder, and form a major part of the care and treatment of people with mental handicap. Some treatments can interfere with patients' basic rights. This is most obviously so in the case of some behaviour modification programmes as dealt with below. However, other forms of psychological treatment can do the same. For example, group therapy has the potential to unleash powerful group pressures which may coerce individuals to act in ways that they find upsetting or distressing, such as discussing sensitive and embarrassing material in a context they would avoid if it were possible to do so. This can also lead to a reasonable concern for confidentiality. No treatment should deprive a patient of food, shelter, water, warmth, a comfortable environment, confidentiality or a reasonable privacy (both physical and in relation to their personal feeling and thoughts).

## Behaviour modification programmes

19.2 The Managers must ensure that the behaviour modification programmes are set out clearly, methodically and in such a way that they can be understood by staff, patients and relatives. Guidelines should include procedures for noting and monitoring their use. Managers should keep themselves well informed of up to date research in this area. A person with sufficient skills in implementing behaviour modification programmes should be available to monitor procedures as well as the progress of patients.

19.3 Any programme to be used should form part of a patient's previously agreed treatment plan. At no time should it be used as a spontaneous reaction to a particular type of behaviour. The patient's consent should always be sought (see 19.7).

19.4 A decision to use any behaviour modification programme for an individual patient should be preceded by a full discussion with the professional staff concerned with the patient.

19.5 Such a programme should be regularly reviewed in the case of each patient, abandoned if it has proved ineffective or otherwise modified if necessary.

19.6 Patients and their relatives should be fully informed of the planned use of any such methods as part of a patient's treatment and the patient's consent should always be sought.

19.7 Although such treatments may proceed in the absence of a patient's consent, this should only be done in certain carefully justified circumstances. If consent is not or cannot be given a locally agreed procedure should be adopted in which the r m o should seek the advice of a suitably qualified person who is not a member of the clinical team responsible for the patient. This will normally be a psychologist although some medical staff, social workers or nurses may have received special training that equips them to supervise psychological procedures. The r m o in these circumstances should notify the management of the hospital, unit or registered mental nursing home of the details of the plan of treatment.

19.8 The r m o can delegate appropriate members of staff to use such programmes. It is therefore the r m o's responsibility to ensure that those to whom he has delegated this have adequate skills and abilities to carry out the procedures to the required standard. The professional managers must ensure that such members of staff have received relevant training and that they know who to turn to for advice where necessary.

**Time-Out**

19.9 Time-out is a technique which removes a patient for a period (lasting no more than 15 minutes) from opportunities to participate in or to obtain positive reinforcers immediately following the occurrence of unacceptable behaviour, normally immediately after an incident of unwanted behaviour, and which then returns the patient to the original environment. It should be seen as one of a range of methods of managing a difficult or disturbed patient, and not as an immediate reaction to such behaviour.

19.10 Hospitals should have clear written policies on the use of time-out as part of their overall policy on general management. The guidelines should include a clear definition of this form of therapy and procedures for noting and monitoring its use on individual patients.

19.11 The important principles of time-out are:
a.   to enable the patient, if his behaviour is changed, to lead a less restricted life within his usual surroundings or any other setting to which he is likely to go;
b.   to form part of a programme where the achievement of positive goals is as much part of the treatment plan as reducing unwanted behaviour;

# 20  Leave of Absence (Section 17)

*(Paras 72–73 of Memorandum)*

20.1 Leave of absence can only be authorized in accordance with the provisions of Section 17 and can be an important part of a patient's treatment plan. The granting of leave should not be used as an alternative to discharging the patient.

20.2 The patient should be fully involved in the decision to grant leave and must of course be asked to consent to any consultation with others (ie relatives, professionals in the community) thought necessary before leave is granted. He should be able to demonstrate to his professional carers that he is likely to be able to cope outside the hospital.

20.3 Leave of absence should be well planned (if possible well in advance) and involve detailed consultation with any appropriate relatives/friends (especially where the patient is to reside with them) and community services which could contribute to its successful implementation. If relatives/friends are to be involved in the patient's care, but he does not consent to their being consulted, leave should not be granted. It should be remembered that duty to provide aftercare (Section 117) applies to patients on leave of absence (see 26.2).

20.4 **The Power to grant leave (Section 17)**
a. **Unrestricted patients.** The decision (which cannot be delegated to another professional) rests with the patient's r m o after necessary consultation (it is not a decision that can be devolved to another doctor), who may impose such condition as he considers necessary. The r m o and other professionals involved should bear in mind, however, that their responsibilities for the patient's care remain the same while he is on leave although they are exercised in a different way. Similarly

the aftercare provision of Section 117 apply to a patient on leave of absence.

b. **Restricted patients.** Any proposal to grant leave has to be approved by the Home Secretary who should be given as much notice as possible, together with full details of the proposed leave.

### Recording and information

20.5 The granting of leave and the conditions attached to it should be recorded in the patient's notes and copies given to the patient, any appropriate relatives/friends and any professionals in the community who need to know.

### Revoking Leave of absence

20.6 An unrestricted patient's leave can be revoked by his r m o where he considers it is necessary, in the interests of the patient's health or safety or for the protection of other people, that the patient should again become an in-patient. The r m o must consider very seriously the reasons for recalling a patient and the consequences or effects that a revocation of leave may have on him. A refusal to take medication should not on its own, for example, be a reason for revocation. The r m o must arrange for a notice in writing revoking the leave to be served on the patient or on the person for the time being in charge of the patient. The reasons for recall should be fully explained to the patient and a record of such explanation placed in the patient's case notes. A restricted patient's leave may be revoked either by his r m o or the Home Secretary.

20.7 It is essential that any appropriate relatives/friends (especially where the patient is residing with them whilst on leave) and other professionals in the community who need to know should have easy access to the patient's r m o if they feel it is essential for consideration to be given to the return of the patient to hospital before the patient's leave is due to end.

**Medical Treatment while on Leave**

20.8 A patient granted leave under Section 17 remains 'liable to be detained' and the provisions of Part IV of the Act continue to apply unless they are a patient referred to in Section 56(1). If it becomes necessary to administer treatment in the absence of the patient's consent under Part IV, the patient should be recalled to hospital.

**Duration of Leave/Renewal of Authority to Detain**

20.9 A period of leave cannot last longer than the duration of the authority to detain which was current when leave was granted. If the patient has not been recalled from leave at the end of the period of detention, he ceases to be liable to be detained. If the r m o decides to recall the patient before the end of the period of detention, he should be satisfied that the patient needs medical treatment in hospital.

20.10 It is unlawful to recall from leave a patient subject to Section 3 solely in order to renew the authority to detain the patient. (R v Hallstrom, Ex Parte W and R v Gardiner, Ex Parte L (1986) 2 WLR 883).

# 21  Absence without Leave (Section 18)

*(Paras 76–80 and 288–289 of Memorandum)*

21.1 The hospital must know the address of a person on leave of absence.

21.2 It is the responsibility of the Managers and of the local authority where guardianship is concerned to ensure that there is a clear written policy in relation to action to be taken when a detained patient goes absent without leave.

21.3 All staff should be familiar with the policy as well as paragraphs 76–80 and 288–289 of the memorandum.

21.4 In particular the policy should include guidance as to:
a.   the immediate action to be taken by any members of staff who become aware that a patient has gone absent without leave, including the requirement that they immediately inform the nurse in charge of the patient's ward who should in turn ensure that the patient's r m o is immediately informed;
b.   the circumstances when a search of the hospital and its grounds should be initiated;
c.   in the case of a patient detained in hospital, circumstances when the police should be informed (having regard to paragraph 288 of the memorandum);
d.   how and when the patient's nearest relative should be informed. In almost all cases the patient's nearest relative should be informed immediately the patient goes absent without leave and any exceptions to this requirement should be clearly set out in the policy;
e.   in the case of someone under guardianship, absent without leave from the place where he is required to reside, who in the local social services authority should be notified immediately.

# 22 Managers Duty to Review Detention

22.1 Managers' Review is the process by which the Managers decide whether a patient can still be detained or can be discharged. It is a different procedure from referral to a Mental Health Review Tribunal and the Managers are responsible for ensuring that patients understand the difference. It is important that no impression is given to patients that any application to a Mental Health Review Tribunal must be preceded by a Manager's Review nor that an application for a Manager's Review negates the patient's rights to apply to a Mental Health Review Tribunal.

22.2 **Managers should undertake a Review**, at any time at their discretion, but must do so:
a. when the patient requests it, unless there has recently been a Review and there is no evidence that the patient's condition or other relevant factors have changed. In these latter circumstances the Managers should investigate, and if there is any doubt a Review should take place;
b. when the patient's r m o makes a report to the Managers, in accordance with Section 20. It is recommended that such reports should be received not less than two weeks prior to the expiry of relevant periods of detention, to enable patient's detention to be reviewed as close as possible to the expiry date of detention;
c. where a patient's r m o makes a report to the Managers in accordance with Section 25(1), barring a nearest relative's discharge application.

## Responsibilities before the Review

22.3 The Managers should ensure that they have reports from the patient's r m o and other relevant disciplines, (such as social workers, psychologists, occupational therapists and nursing staff involved in the patient's care), and they should consult with those professionals concerned with the patient's care, where they think it necessary after reading these reports.

22.4 If the patient consents, Managers must ensure that the patient's nearest and/or most concerned relatives are informed of the Review and asked to comment or to be available for interview in the same way as when the patient is to appear before a Mental Health Review Tribunal. If the patient withholds consent the Managers should ask the appropriate professional concerned with the patient's care to obtain the views of the patient's nearest relative and/or most concerned relatives, and include these in their reports to the Managers.

## The Review

22.5 It is for Managers to decide how to review bearing in mind that the following are necessary:
a.  to balance informality and the gravity of the task; they are reviewing a patient's continued detention;
b.  to help the patient to explain why he wishes to be discharged;
c.  to allow the patient to be accompanied by a member of staff, friend or representative of their choosing, to help put his point of view;
d.  to ensure that the patient's r m o and other relevant professionals are actively and positively questioned by the Managers;
e.  to ensure (subject to 22.4 above) that the patient's nearest/most concerned relatives are given the opportunity to give their point of view or to have it represented through a A S W, C P N or any other such person. The patient must always be offered the opportunity of speaking to the Manager's alone;
f.  if the patient so wishes, to enable the patient and other parties to the review to hear each other's accounts to the Managers and to put questions to each other.

## After the Review

22.6 The Managers should ensure that their decision and the reasons for it are communicated immediately, both orally and in writing to the patient, to any relative who has expressed views, and to the relevant professionals. At least one of the Managers reviewing the patient's detention should explain to the patient in person the reason for their decision, and copies of the reports prepared for the review together with the Managers' written decision letter should be placed in the patient's records.

# 23 Complaints

## General

23.1 The Hospital Complaints Procedures Act 1985 places a duty upon health authorities to investigate any complaint on the part of a patient about any aspect of his treatment. The Department of Health and Welsh Office circulars H C(88)37 and W H C(99)36 respectively, issued in June 1988, set out both the duties and procedures for making complaints and for their investigation.

## The Managers Duties

23.2 The Managers should ensure that as part of their training, all staff are fully conversant not only with the requirements and procedures of the Hospital Complaints Act, but also with the patient's rights to make complaints to the Mental Health Act Commission. In accordance with H C(88)37/W H C(88)36, the Managers must ensure the nomination of a complaints officer within their establishment. One of the duties of this officer should be to log complaints and to ensure that patients are notified of the outcome.

## Staff

23.3 Staff have the responsibility of bringing to the attention of all patients, both orally and in writing, the procedures for making a complaint through the hospital complaints system, and, in relation to detained patients, their rights to complain to the Mental Health Act Commission. If a patient is unable to formulate his complaint, he should be given reasonable assistance to do so by staff. It is the personal responsibility of all members of staff involved in a patient's care to give such assistance where necessary.

## Recording

23.4 All patients' case notes should contain accounts of any complaints made and the outcome in every instance.

# 24 Duties of the Hospital Managers

*(Paras 62–63 of Memorandum)*

24.1 The Managers have important statutory powers, responsibilities and duties concerning detained patients, and are specifically defined in the 1983 Mental Health Act (Section 145).

24.2 The Managers, as defined in the Act are:
a.  members of a district health authority or special health authority, responsible for the administration of the hospital;
b.  the relevant persons registered in respect of a mental nursing home;
c.  any persons appointed by the district health authority or special health authority to any committee or sub-committee of the health authority.

24.3 Officers are those persons properly authorized by the Managers to act on their behalf.

24.4 The health authority should appoint a committee to undertake the duties of the Managers. The committee should comprise informed members of the health authority and other appointed and informed outside persons.

24.5 The Managers may delegate to officers many of their statutory tasks, but they cannot delegate the task of deciding whether a detained patient should be discharged. This decision is personal, exercised by three or more hospital Managers. It is the duty of the Managers to ensure that all officers acting on their behalf are competent to undertake their delegated duties. The Managers retain the ultimate responsibility for the execution of all such duties.

## Admission

24.6 It is the Managers' duty to ensure that the grounds for admitting the patient are valid and reasonable and that all relevant admission documents are in order. The authorized or delegated officer should be able to make judgements based on the facts available regarding the need for admission. Where a patient is admitted under the Act following an application by their nearest relative, the Managers should request the relevant Local Authority Social Services Department to provide them with a social circumstances report (S 14.)

## Transfer

24.7 Subject to the provision of Section 19 and the Mental Health (Hospital, Guardianship and Consent to Treatment) Regulations 1983 (SI 1983 No 893) the Managers can exercise the power to transfer under the Act certain categories of detained patients to another hospital administered by the same authority, to a special health authority or to a hospital in another district. The delegated officers must be able fully to justify their reasons for so doing and ensure that such a transfer is not for punitive reasons.

## Scrutiny and Receipt of Documents

24.8 The Managers should ensure that those formally delegated to receive documents and all those who will be required to scrutinize admission documents have a thorough knowledge of the Act. (See chapter 12).

## Rectification of Documents

24.9 Section 15 of the Act allows for the rectification of certain errors contained in admission documents with the consent of the Managers. It is for the nominated officer to consider whether the papers can be rectified and where possible to take the necessary steps. (See chapter 12).

## Detention, Review, Discharge

24.10 The Managers have the power to discharge certain categories of detained patients. They should ensure that reviews of the patient's detention take place not just at the time stipulated in Section 20 of the Act, but whenever it is thought necessary and in particular, shortly after a patient's admission. (See chapter 22).

## The giving of Information

24.11 The Managers have statutory obligations concerning the giving of information to both detained patients (S 132) and their nearest relatives (S 133) (see chapter 14).

## Correspondence of Patients

24.12 The Managers of the special hospitals have statutory powers (S 134) to withhold outgoing and incoming mail in certain circumstances. The Managers should have a written policy concerning the implementation of these powers; this should be discussed with the Mental Health Act Commission which has the power to review any decision to withhold mail (S 121(7)). The outgoing mail of *any* detained patient may be withheld if the person to whom it is addressed makes such a request in writing to the Managers, the patient's R M O or the Secretary of State.

## Access to Mental Health Review Tribunals

24.13 The Managers should ensure that any patient who wishes to apply to a Mental Health Review Tribunal is given all necessary assistance to progress such an application. They are obliged to refer certain patients detained under Part II of the Act to Mental Health Review Tribunals and it is the responsibility of the Managers to ensure that the necessary arrangements are made. (See paras 209 and 210 of the memorandum).

# 25  Personal Searches

25.1 Authorities should ensure that there is an operational policy on the searching of patients and their belongings. Such a policy should be checked with the health authority's legal advisers.

25.2 It should not be part of such a policy routinely to carry out searches of patients and their personal belongings. If, however, there are lawful grounds for carrying out such a search, the patient's consent should be sought. In undertaking such a search staff should have due regard for the dignity of the person concerned and the need to carry out the search in such a way as to ensure the maximum privacy.

25.3 If the patient does not consent to the search, staff should consult with the Unit General Manager (or such other delegated senior staff (eg senior nurse manager) when he is not available) before undertaking any lawful search. The same principles relating to the patient's dignity and the need for maximum privacy apply. Any such search should be carried out with the minimum force necessary and in the case of a search of a patient's person, unless urgent necessity dictates otherwise, such a search should be carried by a staff member of the same sex.

25.4 If items belonging to a patient are removed, the patient should be informed where these are being kept.

# 26  Aftercare

26.1 The purpose of aftercare is to enable a patient to return to his home or accommodation other than a hospital or nursing home, and to minimize the chances of him needing any future in-patient hospital care.

26.2 Section 117 of the Act 1983 requires health authorities and local authorities, in conjunction with voluntary agencies, to provide aftercare for certain categories of detained patients.

26.3 Health and social services authorities should, together with local voluntary organisations, agree procedures for establishing proper aftercare arrangements. These arrangements should be regularly reviewed and it should be the responsibility of an officer from each of the authorities to ensure that the procedures are working properly. In the case of patients detained under Section 37/41 or Section 47/49 there will be special considerations to be taken into account.

26.4 Proper records should be kept of all those patients for whom S 117 could apply and of those for whom arrangements have been made under Section 117. These records could be in the form of a register.

26.5 Managers in the health service and Directors of Social Services should ensure that all staff are aware of the procedures. Circulars HC(89)5 and LAC(89)7, and the Department of Health booklet 'Discharge of Patients from Hospitals' reminds health and local authorities of the need to plan jointly for aftercare and of the individual responsiblity of the various professionals who are involved in the process. Separate Welsh Office guidance is imminent.

26.6 When a decision has been taken to discharge or grant leave to a patient, it is the responsibility of the r m o to ensure that a discussion takes place to establish a care-plan to organise the management of the patient's continuing health and social care needs. This discussion will usually take place in multi-professional clinical meetings held in psychiatric hospitals and units. If this is not possible, administrative support should be available to the r m o to assist in making arrangements.

**Who should be involved**

26.7 Those who should be involved in the discussion are:

- the patient's r m o;

- a nurse involved in caring for the patient in hospital;

- a social worker specialising in mental health work;

- the G P;

- a C P N;

- a representative of relevant voluntary organisations (where appropriate and available);

- the patient if he wishes and/or a relative or other nominated representative.

26.8 Professionals should be made available to attend. Representatives of housing authorities should be invited if accommodation is an issue. It is important that those who are involved are able to take decisions regarding their own and as far as possible their agencies' involvement. If approval for plans needs to be obtained from more senior levels, (for example, for funding), it is important that this causes no delay to the implementation of the plans.

**Consideration for aftercare**

26.9 Those contributing to the discussion should consider the following issues:
a.   the patient's own wishes and needs;
b.   the views of any relevant relative, friend or supporter of the patient.

c.  the need for agreement with an appropriate representative at the receiving health authority if it is to be different from that of the discharging authority;

d.  the possible involvement of other agencies, e g probation, voluntary organisations;

e.  the establishing of a care-plan, based on proper assessment and clearly identified needs, in which the following issues must be considered and planned for insofar as resources permit: day care arrangements, appropriate accommodation, out-patient treatment, counselling, personal support, assistance in welfare rights, assistance in managing finances, and, if necessary, in claiming benefits;

f.  the appointment of a Key Worker from either of the statutory agencies to monitor the care-plan's implementation, liaise and co-ordinate where necessary and report to the senior officer in their agency any problems that arise which cannot be resolved through normal discussion;

g.  identification of any unmet need.

26.10 The multi-professional discussion should establish an agreed outline of the patient's needs and assets taking into account their social and cultural background, and agree a time-scale for the implementation of the various aspects of the plan. All key people with specific responsibilites with regard to the patient should be properly identified. Once plans are agreed it is essential that any changes are discussed with others involved with the patient before being implemented. The plan should be recorded in writing.

26.11 The care-plan should be regularly reviewed. It will be the responsibility of the Key Worker to arrange reviews of the plan until it is agreed that it is no longer necessary. The senior officer in the Key Worker's agency responsible for Section 117 arrangements should ensure that all aspects of the procedure are followed.

# 27 Part III of the Mental Health Act – Patients Concerned with Criminal Proceedings

## *Leaving Hospital*

### Discharge/Return to Court

**27.1 Conditionally Discharged Restricted Patients – Supervision**
Those involved in the supervision of a conditionally discharged restricted patient should have copies of and be familiar with 'Supervision and After-care of Conditionally Discharged Restricted Patients' (HO/DoH notes of guidance (1987)) and D H S S circular LASSL(80)7.

### Recall

27.2 If a conditionally discharged restricted patient requires hospital admission, it will not always be necessary for the Home Secretary to recall the patient to hospital. For example:
a.  The patient may be willing to accept treatment informally. In these circumstances however, care should be taken to ensure that the possibility of the patient being recalled does not render the patient's consent to informal admission invalid by reason of duress.
b.  In some cases it may be appropriate to consider admitting the patient under Part II of the Act as an alternative.
c.  It may not always be necessary to recall the patient to the same hospital from which he was conditionally discharged. In some cases recall to a hospital with a lesser (or greater) degree of security will be appropriate.

27.3 When a recall is being considered this should be discussed between the doctor and the social supervisor.

27.4 If a patient is recalled, the person taking him into custody should explain that he is being recalled to hospital by the Home

Secretary and that a fuller explanation will be given to him later. As soon as possible after admission to hospital, and in any event within 72 hours of admission, the r m o or his deputy should explain to the patient the reason for his recall and ensure, in so far as the patient's mental state allows, that he understands. The patient should also be informed that his case will be referred to a Mental Health Review Tribunal within one month.

27.5 The patient's r m o should ensure that:

– the patient is given assistance to inform his legal adviser (if any);

– subject to the patient's consent, his nearest relative and/or other appropriate relative or friend is told.

### 27.6 Patients on Remand/Subject to Interim Hospital Orders

All professionals concerned with ensuring the return to court of a patient on remand or under an interim hospital order should be familiar with the contents of paragraphs 31–33 of Home Office circular number 71/1984. When a patient has been admitted on remand or subject to an interim hospital order, it is the responsibility of the hospital to return the patient to court as required. The court should give adequate notice of the hearing. The hospital should liaise with the courts in plenty of time to affirm the arrangements for escorting the patient to/from hospital. The hospital will be responsible for providing a suitable escort for the patient when he is taken from the hospital to the court and should plan for the provision of necessary staff to do this. The assistance of the police may be requested if necessary. Once on the court premises, the patient will come under the supervision of the police or prison officers there.

# 28  People with Mental Handicap

## General

28.1 The guidance given elsewhere in the Code applies to patients with mental handicap (often referred to as learning difficulties). This chapter gives guidance on a number of particular issues of importance to this group of patients.

28.2 Very few people with mental handicap are detained under the Act. Some admission sections can only be considered where the person with a mental handicap falls within the legal definition of 'mental impairment' or 'severe mental impairment'. People with mental handicap can of course be considered for admission under the Act when they are suffering from another form of mental disorder (for example mental illness).

## Communication

28.3 The assessment of a person with mental handicap requires special consideration to be given to communication with a person being assessed. Where possible the A S W should have had experience of working with people with a mental handicap or be able to call upon someone who has. It is important that someone who knows the patient, and can communicate with him is present at the assessment. Someone with a knowledge of Makaton or other communication systems may be of assistance.

## Assessment

28.4 It is desirable that no patient should be classified under the Act as mentally impaired or severely mentally impaired in the absence of a formal psychological assessment as evidence of severe or significant impairment of intelligence. This assessment should be part of a complete appraisal by medical, nursing, social work and psychology professionals and, wherever appropriate, by those with experience in mental handicap. This procedure is also desirable where it is proposed that a patient is to be detained under Section 2 on the grounds of mental disorder in the form of arrested or incomplete development of mind, although the urgency of the case may preclude this.

## Mental Impairment/Severe Mental Impairment (legally defined in Section 1)

28.5 The identification of an individual who falls within these legal categories is a matter for clinical judgement, guided by current professional practice and subject to the relevant legal requirements. Those assessing the patient must be satisfied that the person concerned displays a number of characteristics difficult to define in practice. This section of the chapter sets out guidance in relation to the key factors or components of these legal categories.

*Incomplete or arrested development of mind.* This implies that the features that determine the handicap were present at some stage which permanently prevented the usual maturation of intellectual and social development. It excludes persons whose handicap derives from accident, injury or illness occurring after that point usually accepted as complete development.

*Severe or significant impairment of Intelligence.* The judgement as to the presence of this particular characteristic must be made on the basis of reliable and careful assessment.

*Severe or significant impairment of social functioning.* The evidence of the degree and nature of social competence should be based on reliable and recent observations, preferably from a number of sources such as social workers, nurses and psychologists. Such evidence should include the results of one or more social functioning assessment tests.

*Abnormally aggressive behaviour.* Any assessment of this category should be based on observations of behaviour which lead to a conclusion that the actions are outside the usual range of aggressive behaviour, and which cause actual damage and/or real distress occurring recently or persistently or with excessive severity.

*Irresponsible conduct.* The assessment of this characteristic should be based on an observation of behaviour which shows a lack of responsibility, a disregard of the consequences of action taken, and where the results cause actual damage or real distress, either recently or persistently or with excessive severity.

# 29 Children and Young People Under the Age of 18

## General

29.1 The Code of Practice applies to all patients including those under 18. This chapter gives guidance on a number of issues of particular importance to those under the age of 18. There is no minimum age limit for admission to hospital under the Act.

29.2 Practice for this age group should be guided by the following principles:
a.  young people should be kept as fully informed as possible about their care and treatment; their views and wishes must always be taken into account;
b.  unless statute specifically overrides, young people should be regarded as having the right to make their own decisions (and in particular treatment decisions) when they have sufficient 'understanding and intelligence';
c.  any intervention in the life of a young person, considered necessary by reason of their mental disorder, should be the least restrictive possible and result in the least possible segregation from family, friends, community and school.

29.3 The legal framework governing the admission to hospital and treatment of young people under the age of 18 (and in particular those under the age of 16) is complex and it is the responsibility of all professionals and the relevant local health authorities to ensure that there is sufficient guidance available to those responsible for the care of children and young people.

29.4 Whenever the care and treatment of somebody under the age of 16 is being considered, the following questions (amongst many others) need to be asked:

a.  who is legally responsible for decisions affecting this child, and who has the authority to make such decisions? It is essential that those responsible for the child or young person's care always request copies of any statutory orders (wardship, care order, custody order, guardianship order, access arrangements, etc) for reference on the ward;

b.  if the child is in the custody of parents who are separated, which parent has custody, or is the custody shared?;

c.  what is the capability of the child to make their own decisions in terms of emotional maturity, intellectual capacity and psychological state?;

d.  where a parent refuses consent to treatment, how sound are the reasons and on what grounds are they made?;

e.  how 'necessary' is treatment for the child?;

f.  how viable would be treatment of an under 16 year old living at home if there was no parental consent and no statutory orders.

## Informal Admission to Hospital by Parents or Guardians

29.5 *Children under 16.* Parents or guardians may arrange for the admission of children under the age of 16 to hospital as informal patients. Where a doctor concludes, however, that a child under the age of 16 has the capacity to make such a decision for himself, there is no right to admit him to hospital informally or to keep him there on an informal basis against his will.

Where a child is willing to be so admitted, but the parents/guardian object, their views should be accorded serious consideration and given due weight. It should be remembered that recourse to law to stop such an admission could be sought.

29.6 Young people aged 16–18. Anyone in this age group who is 'capable of expressing his own wishes' can admit or discharge himself as an informal patient to or from hospital, irrespective of the wishes of his parents or guardian.

## Consent to Medical Treatment

29.7 The following guidance applies to young people who are not detained under the Act:

a.  *Under 16.* If a child has 'sufficient understanding and intelligence' they can take decisions about their own medical treatment in the same way as an adult. Otherwise the permission of parents/guardians must be sought (save in emergencies where only the treatment necessary to end the emergency should be given). If parents/guardians do not consent to treatment, consideration should be given to both the use of child care legislation and the Mental Health Act before coming to a final conclusion as to what action should be taken. In complex cases wardship may be the preferable course to take for so long as wardship continues to exist.

b.  The same principles concerning consent apply where the under 16 year old is in the care of a local authority. Where such a child does not have sufficient 'understanding and intelligence' to take their own treatment decisions, the legal authority to authorise any treatment is vested in the care authority. Their legal obligation to consult the children's parents depends upon how the child was brought into care. Wherever possible, parents should be consulted. Where children are wards of court, then the consent of the High Court must be sought. In an emergency consent may be obtained retrospectively (but this should be regarded as wholly exceptional).

c.  *Young people aged 16 and 17.* Young people in this age group who have the capacity to make their own treatment decisions can do so in the same way as adults (Section 8 Family Law Reform Act, 1969). Where such a young person does not have this capacity the authorisation of either parent, guardian or care authority (whichever has the lawful authority in relation to the particular young person) must be obtained. The consent of the High Court must be obtained in the case of wards of court.

## Parent/Guardians Consent

29.8 The fact that a child or young person has been informally admitted by parents/guardians should not lead professionals to assume that they have consented to any treatment regarded as 'necessary'. Consent should be sought for each aspect of the child's care and treatment as it arises. 'Blanket' consent forms must not be used.

## Children in Care placed in 'Secure Accommodation'

29.9 Where a child in care is placed by his care authority in accommodation where liberty is restricted (for example N H S secure units or a private nursing home) application must be made to the juvenile court within 72 hours if the restriction is to last beyond that period (Section 21A of the Child Care Act 1980). This provision does not apply to such children who are detained under the Act. Where the child is a ward of court, the local authority must obtain the permission of the High Court prior to any restriction of liberty.

## Information

29.10 The advice concerning the giving of information (see Chapter 14) applies with equal force to patients under the age of 18. In particular where such patients are detained under the Act, it is important that assistance is given to enable their legal representation at any Mental Health Review Tribunal.

## Confidentiality

29.11 Young people's legal rights to confidentiality should be strictly observed. It is important that all professionals have a clear understanding of their obligations of confidentiality to young people and that any limits to such an obligation are made clear to a young person who has the capacity to understand them.

## Placement

29.12 Children and young people admitted to hospital should not be placed in adult wards (nor should children enter adolescent facilities or vice versa unless their development level makes this appropriate) unless the condition of the patient warrants such admission in an emergency and no alternative is available.

## Complaints

29.13 Children and young people in hospital (both as informal and detained patients) and their parents or guardians should have ready access to existing complaints procedures, which should be drawn to their attention on their admission to hospital. The Managers should appoint an officer whose responsibility it is to ensure that this is done and to assist any complainant.

## Education

29.14 All children and young people in hospital should receive appropriate education. All children and young people who are informal patients have a right to full-time education from the age of 5 to 19. Where such people are detained they do not have such a legal right, although local education authorities have the power to make arrangements for such children to receive the benefit of education facilities provided by the authority.

## Welfare of certain hospital patients

29.15. Local authorities should ensure that they arrange for visits to be made to certain patients (including children and young persons in respect of whom the rights and powers of parents have been vested in the local authority by virtue of Sections 3 and 10 of the Child Care Act 1980) in hospital or nursing home in England and Wales as required by Section 116 and that they take such other steps in relation to the patient while in hospital or nursing home as would be expected to be taken by his parents.

## GLOSSARY

The Sections referred to are those of the 1983 Mental Health Act.

| | |
|---|---|
| Act, the | Mental Health Act 1983 |
| Applicant, the | The patient's nearest relative or an Approved Social Worker (S 11) |
| Approved Social Worker (A S W) | Defined in S 145(1) (but see S 114) |
| Forms | Details of the forms referred to in the Code of Practice can be found in schedule 1 of Mental Health (Hospital, Guardianship and Consent to Treatment) Regulations 1983 (S I 1983 No 893) |
| Hospital | Defined in S 145(1) |
| Local Social Services Authority | Defined in S 145(1) |
| Managers, the | Defined in S 145(1) |
| Memorandum, the | Mental Health Act 1983, Memorandum on Parts I to VI, VIII and X. Department of Health (H M S O 1987) |
| Medical Treatment | See S 145(1) |
| Mental disorder (and statutory sub categories of mental disorder) | Defined in S 1 |
| Mental Nursing Home | Defined in S 145(1) |
| Nearest Relative | Defined in S 26 |
| Nominated Medical Attendant | Defined in S 34(1) |

| | |
|---|---|
| Patient | Defined in S 145(1) |
| Place of Safety | Defined in S 135(6) |
| Regulations | A number of regulations (also known as statutory instruments) have been made under powers given in the Act. The most important, for the purposes of understanding this Code are the Mental Health (Hospital, Guardianship and Consent to Treatment) Regulations 1983 (S I 1983 No 893) |
| Responsible Medical Officer (R M O) | Defined in S 34 |

# STATUTORY REFERENCES

## Child Care Act 1980

Section

| | |
|---|---|
| 3 | 29.15 |
| 10 | 29.15 |
| 21A | 29.9 |

## Mental Health Act 1983

Section

| | |
|---|---|
| 1 | 2.18, 28.5 |
| 2 | 3.11, 5.1–5.4, 28.4 |
| 3 | 3.11, 5.1–5.4 |
| 4 | 6.1–6.8 |
| 5(2) | 8.1–8.12 |
| 5(3) | 8.13–8.16 |
| 5(4) | 9.1–9.10 |
| 7 | 13.1–13.10 |
| 11 | 2.13 |
| 12 | 2.36–2.38, 4.1 |
| 13(2) | 2.11 |
| 13(4) | 2.27, 2.32–2.33 |
| 14 | 24.6 |
| 15 | 12.1–12.5, 24.9 |
| 17 | 20.1–20.10 |
| 18 | 21.1–21.4 |
| 20 | 22.2, 24.10 |
| 25(1) | 22.2c |
| 26 | 2.13 |
| 29 | 2.14 |
| 35–55 (Part III) | 3.1–3.13 |
| | 7.1–7.3 |
| | 13.10 |
| | 17.1–17.5 |
| | 27.1–26.7 |
| 56–64 (Part IV) | 16.1–16.38 |
| 116 | 29.15 |
| 117 | 26.1–26.11 |

## Police and Criminal Evidence Act 1984

Section

# INDEX

**Admission:**

**Aftercare:**

**Approved Doctors:**

**Approved Social Worker:**

**Assessment:**

Printed in the United Kingdom for HMSO
Dd293072 2/91 C70 G443 10170